Thieves & Kings

ISBN: 0-9681025-2-2

Printed in Canada

I Box Publishing welcomes any comments or questions at the
above address, and may publish/answer them in the letters
pages of the on-going comic book series, available at finer
comic shops everywhere.

Second printing 2000

Thieves & Kings is a long story which spans several books.
At the time of this printing, three of those books had been
produced, and a number of original comics were still available. If you are interested in purchasing copies directly
from *I Box Publishing*, your order would be happily filled.
Send a letter asking for ordering information or check out
the company website for the most current pricing. (Both
address are listed above.)

Introduction

Way back when I was just setting up my publishing company and doing the lay-out designs for the first couple of issues, my best friend in the world, Carson Court, told me that he wanted to handle all the shipping and receiving for I Box Publishing.

I was a little worried about this; there's a saying which advises people to never mix business and friendship. —Which essentially means, if it becomes necessary to do something cut-throat or unpleasant business-wise, you don't want to have to do it to your friend. And conversely, you don't want your friend thinking that he can get away with only doing a half-hearted job, believing that you'll feel too uncomfortable to yell at him. These issues worried me a lot, and they seemed like good reasons to avoid working with Carson.

But something about this logic bothered me. It seemed too simple and rather too cynical, and it left me feeling ugly. I've never had any respect for companies who treat their employees poorly. I prefer to buy things from organizations which foster a healthy corporate culture; the ones that don't have or need unions. —And people who try to get away with doing a lazy, poor job, are usually people who don't have any respect for their employers; in fact, they usually feel downright animosity. So after considering things more carefully I decided, "You know, I think this, 'never mix business and friendship' advice is probably a symptom of something else. Knowing Carson, and knowing myself, I'm not sure it applies."

So I took a deep breath and wrote Carson a check to get the ball rolling. He was going to clear out some space in his spare garage, (a small separate building on his property dubbed for some inexplicable reason, 'the White Garage'). When the space was cleared, he would then build a set of shelves in which to stack boxes of books. It was a sound plan, I thought, but it quickly became something different when Carson decided that clearing out the garage was an insurmountable task and that he'd instead be keeping my boxes inside his house. This made me nervous, but I forced myself to remain calm. —One thing I've learned about Carson is that the best way for him to achieve anything is to simply leave him to his own bizarre devices. Invariably, he solves problems with better results than most people could ever hope to achieve. So I just sat back and relaxed, curious as to how Carson was going to make this work, space around his house being somewhat. . , limited. And not because he has a small house.

This bears some explanation. . .

Carson's father, among his many jobs, spent several years working as a professional magician and a lot of his old stuff now lives with his son. You can literally step on disappearing dove tricks and disembodied thumbs and strange mirror contraptions when trying to walk around the place. There are also bits and pieces of computer everywhere. Carson likes to take them apart and put them back together again according to his specific tastes and whatever esoteric digital technology he's into at the time. There are also wood, plumbing and cement working tools scattered about. And test tubes and photographic equipment. And a Bunsen burner, a microscope and a big IBM wall clock from the fifties which he rescued from our old highschool before they tore it down, (and has set permanently to 3:16 'get to go home' time). He has a leather-working kit from last century and Japanese cooking knives from this one. He also has an Italian pasta machine and an Israeli gas mask, mountain climbing gear, book binding equipment, a dozen musical instruments of every size, (about the only things he doesn't actually know how to use). —Halloween just came and went; Carson can dress up like Death if he wanted to; he has a seven foot scythe. (Although he's never dressed up as Death. He would rather dress up like Santa Claus, and of course, he has a full Santa suit should the mood strike. And it sometimes does, even when it's not Christmas. Just to give an example). And all of this stuff is jostled together with ten thousand other objects of various fascination. And books, books, and more books; mostly reference. —A reference book is the greatest source of power in the world, he told me once. With a reference book, you can do practically anything.

It's true. Carson is the only guy I know in the whole universe who owns a three hundred and fifty pound Warner Brother's cartoon style anvil. And a coal burning forge to go along with it, all set up in his backyard. —He felt like being a blacksmith one day, and read a book all about it.

Quinton's tower was meant to approximate something of this jaw-dropping corner of reality in which Carson lives. But only *something* of it.   —Partly because it would be fantastically hard to draw, and partly because I wanted to give my characters enough space to perform their scenes. And anyway, I don't think I'd trust Quinton with the shipping and receiving of my books. Carson and Quinton, while I like them both, are by no means the same. For one thing, Carson is very, *very* good at shipping and receiving. I don't think I've been billed *once* by any of those border-pirate brokerage companies in nearly two years. If you want to do that legally, it takes some serious talent. And perhaps it *does* even take a little bit of magic.

But boy! Does Carson ever live with boxes! Boxes come in, and boxes go out. He puts them in his living room and he puts them in his spare bedroom. He puts them in his kitchen and he puts them in his stairwell, I've even seen boxes stored in his *fireplace.* Carson's life often resembles a giant game of Tetris. Every now and again I'll say something like, "You know, if you'd like, we can rent a dumpster and I'll help you clear out the White Garage. . ." But he just laughs. "You don't want to go in there, Mark. The White Garage is beyond even our combined abilities."

Needless to say, my working arrangement with Carson has turned out very well. Through all of Carson's mountains of unconventional knowledge and problem solving expertise, and through the dependable nature which has made him an immovable, deeply respected and beloved foundation stone for his entire family, through *all* of these elements, my little publishing company has benefitted. And the work I toil upon day after day has also been changed. I have no doubt *Thieves & Kings* would be a much lesser affair without him.

Hm.

It occurs to me. . . There is a good chance that this very copy of the *Blue Book* you're now reading has been stored in the real-world equivalent of Quinton's tower.

How many fantasy books come with *that* level of service?

I'll let you ponder.

Take care, and enjoy the story.

Mark Oakley
Toronto, Canada
November, 1998

When We Last Left Our Hero. . .

Chapter 1

The letter, old and worn, was written on a single length of scroll paper. It was penned out in the rather scratchy and unaccomplished hand of one who probably should have learned better but had never likely been able to sit still long enough to do so. (A condition most unsuitable for a wizard.) The words however, had a confident, solid look to them and Heath knew at once it was Quinton's work.

She stepped back from the open chest and took a shaky breath. Pushing a wet hand through wet hair, she began to read, while all about her the green and golden world throbbed with heat and insects.

The letter went like this. . .

Hello Heath,

I apologize for the abrupt method of travel and for the puddle. I hope it wasn't too muddy. I would have arranged that you arrive through a nicer bit of water, but there were squid monsters living in most of them.

You will be happy to know that we fared very well in the secret war. Capturing Jurid dealt a severe blow to Locumire's forces. We owe a great deal to you for that. Davin and Finnly and your aunt and uncle Jay miss you very much, but after I explained things more clearly, they all understood why you had to leave. —It did, however, take a bit more effort with Mr. and Mrs. Jay. (Regular adults always have a rather difficult time accepting the magical aspect of things. —Along with nearly everybody else, they thought the war was just a matter of soldiers and politics. Even after the king helped me explain it!).

Shortly after you escaped your sister and travelled to the garden, I stole back the chest of charms from the enemy, and carried the items this time to the king myself. Davin and Finnly rode with me. They are both heros. The king disallowed the marriages of his military officers and several of the controlling lords in the lowlands to Locumire's girls. With my assistance and the Minister's Alludicator, (which we also stole), the spells were broken.

The Battle of Millbrook was not so clean in the winning, however. And Shoals was much worse. Locumire had influence over several powerful baronages by that point, and when we arrived to put an end to her, we found her forces quite formidable. We did manage to out-manoeuvre them however, and the king's elite guard led our troops to victory. Locumire, I am sure, knew right away that she was going to lose, but she was not in a reasoning state of mind at that point. She fought the bitter fight and did not surrender. Many people died that day. Luckily for us, your sister held back from the conflict. I don't think even she knows why, but it is a good thing that she did. Sally can be the angel of death when the will consumes her. Without you, we could not have matched them if she had decided to lend herself to the battle.

I think that maybe she has come upon that tablet you and Progenis wrote an age or two ago, and it has set her to thinking. I suggest it might be this, because I discovered recently that the stone was found washed up on the shores of Panjir with nearly all of the writing still intact. Perhaps the tablet was not so dangerous as we thought? The serpents seemed not to think so. Still, your sister is very dangerous. —Even where you will be going after you leave the garden. You should keep away from her. Any tempting on your part, and you might find yourself on the wrong end of her unhappiness. I planned for things as best I could, but there is still much about her that concerns me.

There are several other important things which have slipped my mind as I write this, but do not worry. I promised I would let you know what was going on, and I have held to that. About two years before the battle, my memory returned to me in a rare flash of clarity, and I spent some time to write down a full accounting and history of everything important since before you and your sister were first born; nearly three hundred of your lives ago. It contains information that even Progenis was unable to recall from Glamoth's peak. I would like to read this book myself. (I will have forgotten most of it by the time you get this message.) You must carry it with you when you come, so that we might read through it together. I think it may prove our saving grace. Of course, it will be a bit heavy to travel with, but I know you will do your best. Also, there are several large fold-out maps in the back cover, one of which is of the garden you are now in. (The little red dot is you.) That map will show you how to get to Rogue's tea house tower where your paladin, Rubel, will be waiting. It also shows how to leave the garden once you have found him.

So that's it. Good luck. I will be waiting for you in Highborn of Oceansend.

Your friend,

Q.Z.

P.S. Don't go into any more water until you are ready to leave the garden, and have Rubel deal with any squid monsters first. Also, make sure you stay off the grass, and don't eat any fruit or smell any flowers while you are there. The apples are particularly bad.

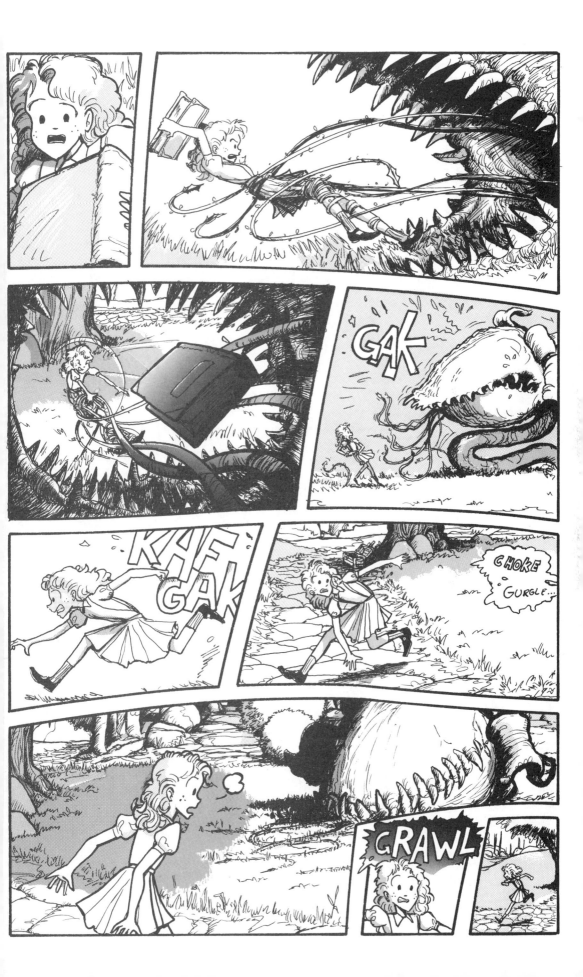

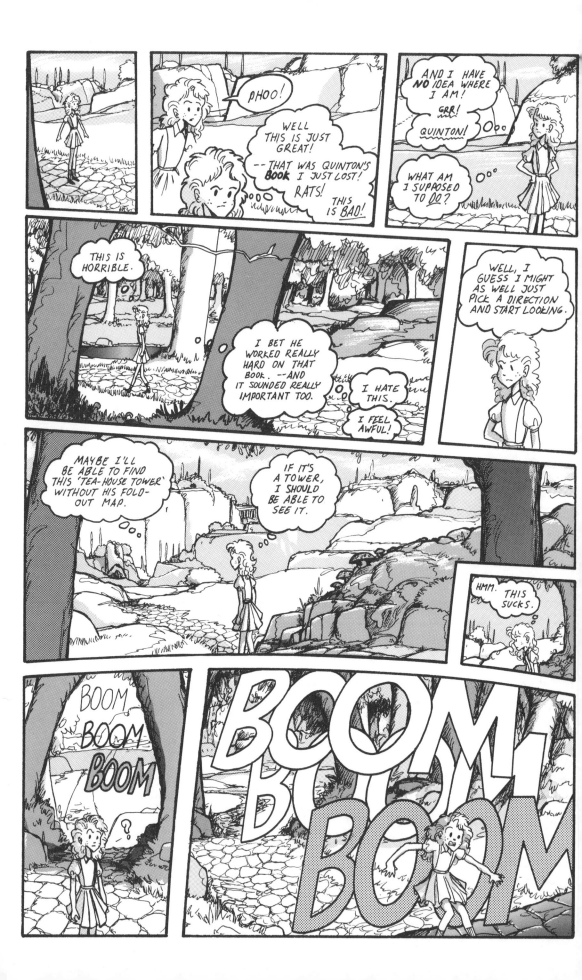

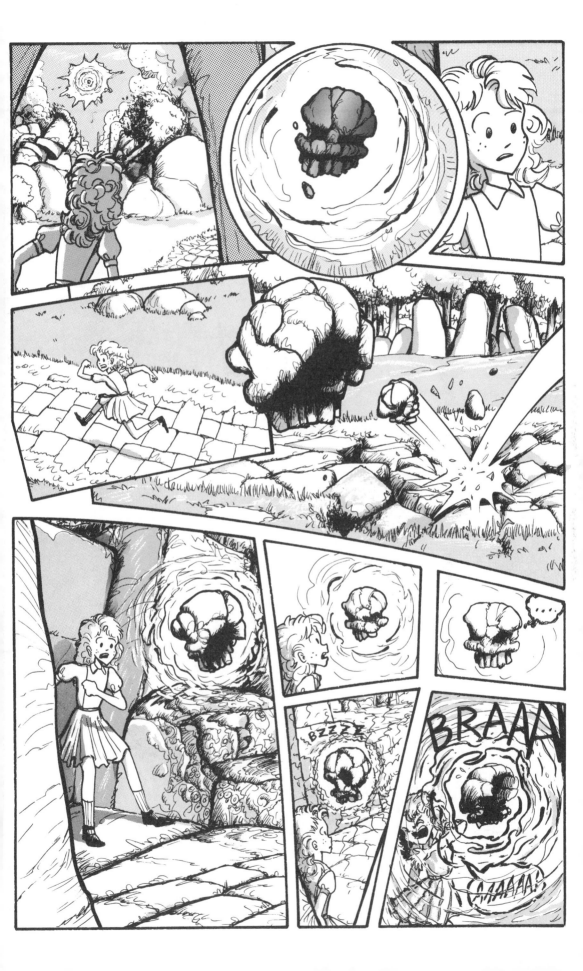

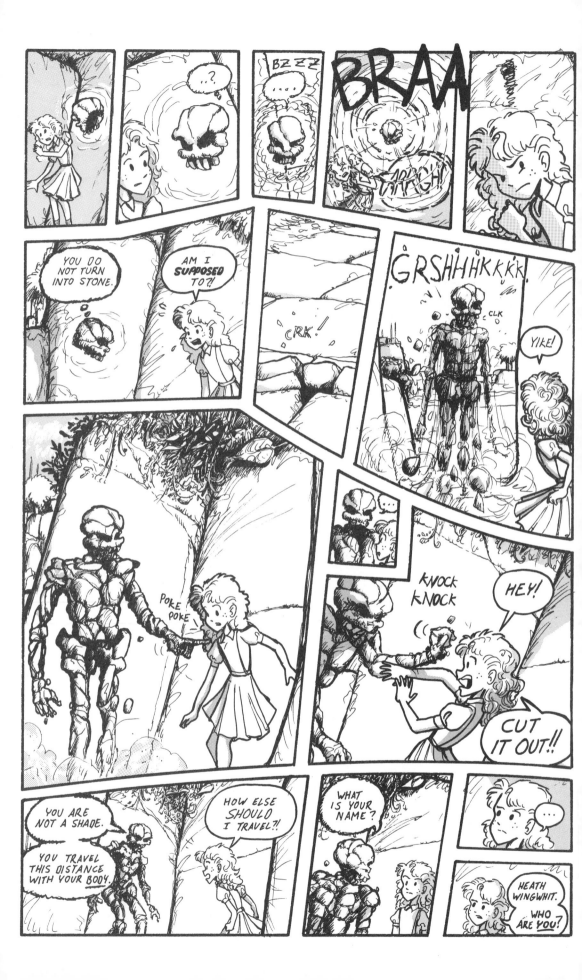

WINGWHIT? I DO NOT KNOW THIS NAME.

YOU ARE A SORCERESS?

SORT OF.

YOU ARE NOT WELCOME HERE.

YOU ARE NOT SUMMONED BY LEAVE OF MY MASTER.

MY MASTER WILL HAVE NO WINGWHITS WHO BRING THEIR BODIES TO TRAVEL!

THE MOUNTAIN WORM WILL HAVE NO GUESTS IN HIS GARDEN.

NOTHING NICE OR SWEET FOR HIM!

NO WINGWHITS!

I'M SORRY.

I DIDN'T REALLY COME HERE ON PURPOSE...

NO WINGWHITS!

NOT FOR THE WORM! -- ONLY THIEVES AND GORGONS AND THINGS HE DOESN'T LIKE!

EXCEPT FOR SALLY'S THIEF...

NO, NO! NO NICE THINGS FOR HER EITHER. — NO FRIENDS FOR SALLY!

IN THIS ALONE DOES THE WORM GET HIS WAY!

ROGUE HATES THIEVES, AND KATH HATES SALLY'S THIEF.

SO THEY HATES A THIEF TOGETHER!

BUT THE MOUNTAIN WORM IS SCARED TO KILL HIS THIEF.

I AM NOT!

WILL TURN THIEVES TO STONE, WILL I!

CANNOT HIDE IN ROGUE'S TOWER FOREVER, CAN HE!

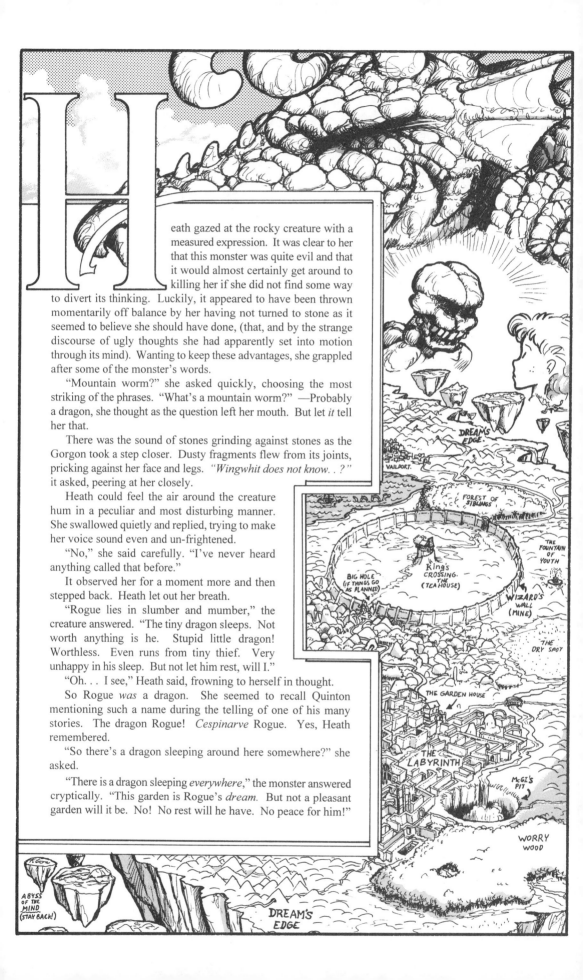

Heath gazed at the rocky creature with a measured expression. It was clear to her that this monster was quite evil and that it would almost certainly get around to killing her if she did not find some way to divert its thinking. Luckily, it appeared to have been thrown momentarily off balance by her having not turned to stone as it seemed to believe she should have done, (that, and by the strange discourse of ugly thoughts she had apparently set into motion through its mind). Wanting to keep these advantages, she grappled after some of the monster's words.

"Mountain worm?" she asked quickly, choosing the most striking of the phrases. "What's a mountain worm?" —Probably a dragon, she thought as the question left her mouth. But let *it* tell her that.

There was the sound of stones grinding against stones as the Gorgon took a step closer. Dusty fragments flew from its joints, pricking against her face and legs. *"Wingwhit does not know. . ?"* it asked, peering at her closely.

Heath could feel the air around the creature hum in a peculiar and most disturbing manner. She swallowed quietly and replied, trying to make her voice sound even and un-frightened.

"No," she said carefully. "I've never heard anything called that before."

It observed her for a moment more and then stepped back. Heath let out her breath.

"Rogue lies in slumber and mumber," the creature answered. "The tiny dragon sleeps. Not worth anything is he. Stupid little dragon! Worthless. Even runs from tiny thief. Very unhappy in his sleep. But not let him rest, will I."

"Oh. . . I see," Heath said, frowning to herself in thought.

So Rogue *was* a dragon. She seemed to recall Quinton mentioning such a name during the telling of one of his many stories. The dragon Rogue! *Cespinarve* Rogue. Yes, Heath remembered.

"So there's a dragon sleeping around here somewhere?" she asked.

"There is a dragon sleeping *everywhere*," the monster answered cryptically. "This garden is Rogue's *dream.* But not a pleasant garden will it be. No! No rest will he have. No peace for him!"

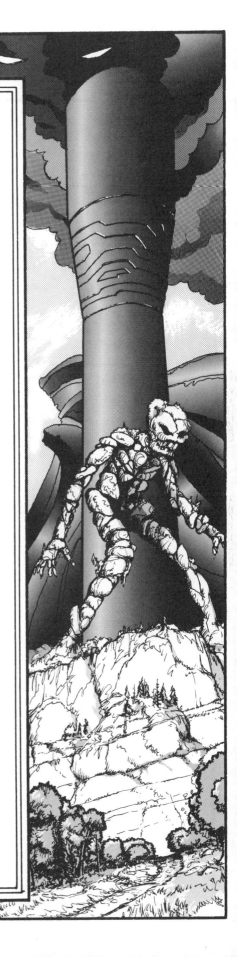

eath glanced at the vast green landscape just beyond the Gorgon. This whole place was somebody's dream-land? She pondered briefly and found that oddly enough, she could accept this. Particularly if it were a *dragon's* dream-land. Dragons were certainly magical enough. Indeed, it occurred to her that this might well have been the very same place she had dreamed while sleeping beneath Quinton's tree. . . When she had experienced her vision of the multitude of ghosts and the giant cat. And the boy, Rubel and the Shadow Lady who would not fight her. Yes. Perhaps they had *all* come to this particular dream-world to meet. To a powerful, dragon's dream, lucid enough to contain them all.

What else had the stone gorgon said. . ?

"That lady with the thief," she asked, "was she wearing a black cloak with a black bow on her chest?" Of course she was, she thought. The lady who was her *sister*. And the thief who was most likely the boy named Rubel she was supposed to find. But again, let the monster tell her that.

It didn't.

Instead, it grew agitated by the question. It shuffled and muttered and then at last bellowed, "I am *Klachilies*. Cast by the very hand of the Furious Lord himself! Very powerful, am I! Turn men to stone, do I! Chase thieves and make them duck, do I! But I will get! Not hide in drinking tea house forever. Not dead, like poisoned kings! And no Sorceress has he anymore! No Shadow Queen. She has turned to *dust!* I smell her on the wind! I will turn the thief to stone before he leaves, or he will die where his body lies in the waking world beyond! Dead or stone, he will remain here forever!"

"Is the thief a boy with blondish-brownish hair?"

"Blondish-brownish-smallish-boyish. . . Just a little thief. But *Rogue* is scared of him. Scared of thieves is he! He hates little thief! And so does Ramanious! The thief melts the heart of his queen. Melts her heart of ice, so hates the thief, he does! But I will kill the little thief. Cannot stay in drinking tea house for ever. Cannot stay in tower! Not so safe is he! Not from Ramanious."

"Who?" Heath asked, now intrigued despite her treacherous situation. "Ramanious? Who is that?"

"Ooh!" the gorgon swooned at the name. "Great is Kath! Beautiful and terrible is he. Thunders and Wonders does he! Up from the stone he pulls me. Up to fight dragons! Kill and slay! Am strong and mighty in the mountains! The black tower is mine to guard! None get in! None get out! Round and round I walk. And shadow and smoke with blades of soot, Kath's shadow walks with me! We kill all manner of beast do we. Bird and bone, and dragons do we slay, side by side, under the eye of Ramanious Kath we do! We two are mighty, shadow and stone and smoke! Long and long and long ago. . ."

Shadow and smoke?" Heath asked, blinking. "That sounds like Jurid. You were killing dragons with *Jurid*?"

"Jurid, yes! We slew them one after another, after *another*. But little Cespinarve Rogue thinks he will show the proper dragons he is not so small and weak! Thinks he will save them all! Thinks they will love him now! Fights like rats and beetles. Moves and twitches! Is long fight, but no match for shadow and stone. No match for Jurid and Klachilies! Hate Rogue! Hate him! Hate him! Hate him! But does not stay to fight! Is afraid and small! Bites Wonderful Ramanious! Bites him through his *shadow*! Dragons are much of very vile magic to do such things! Hate Rogue, I do!"

"He *bit* Kath? He bit your master?"

"Rat and Worm! Little Rogue! Bites him unexpected, and runs and runs and runs and runs away. Hate him! Hate him! Hate him!"

"Hm. That's not too bad for a little dragon. That sounds very brave."

"IS BAD! Is very bad! Ramanious bleeds, and nasty Rogue's poison burns through Master's veins so that he sleeps for long many years. Long years ago. But sent me! Through the mountains, Kath did! With his last breath commands me."

"Commands you?" Heath asked.

"Through the mountains. One after one, two after two, gully after gorge. And up slumping Rogue and into his dragon's ear. Now in his *dreams* I hide! No peace will Rogue find here. Not in a garden. Not here!"

"Hum! Quinton never told me any of *this*," Heath huffed. "I sort of thought Cespinarve Rogue was a *bad* dragon. From everything *he* said. But now Rogue just sounds small and unhappy. And brave too, if he fought both you and Jurid and managed to defeat this Kath fellow."

But the Gorgon Klachilies did not hear this. It cocked its head at Quinton's name.

"Quinton?" it demanded invidiously. "Filthy-vile *Kaluvinar?* You be *Kaluvinar's* sorceress?"

Heath hesitated, caught fearful for a moment, remembering what it was she stood before. But then a spurt of unexpected confidence struck her, along with a touch of irritation.

"What if I am?" she asked.

Klachilies practically stamped at this.

"Will turn you to stone then, will I! To *stone!*"

"You already tried that."

The gorgon glowered to think for a moment.

"Will *kill* you then! Not *always* could I turn beast to stone. Killing done in *many* ways! Will smash and mash your pretty head! Skin and bone no match for stone!"

As frightful a threat as this was, for some reason it only made Heath laugh. And not just *any* laugh, but one of those abrupt, 'you don't scare me' laughs. A real one. Heath *really* wasn't scared, and this caught her entirely by surprise. —It had quite an effect on the gorgon as well, who was unused to responses of this sort.

"You can try," Heath went on, "but I'm a sorceress. And for your information, Jurid just tried to kill me this morning, and you can ask him what happened if you like. If you can *find* him!"

"Jurid?" the gorgon stopped. "You fought with *Jurid?"*

"That's right. And I won."

Klachilies considered her words with some gravity. Perhaps able to see the sincerity in her expression, It shuffled in the gravel for a moment, looking down and up in consternation, and then asked cautiously, "What did you do? What can a little girl do to a *Jurid?"*

"I caught him and put him in a bottle," she said simply.

The gorgon observed her face. "Little sorceress put Jurid into a *bottle?"*

"With a glass stopper and wire to hold him in. He won't be getting out very soon, I can tell you." Heath thought for a moment, judged her luck, and then added slowly, "And maybe. . . I should do something to *you* as well. . . If you want to fight me so bad. Maybe I should turn you into some mud. How would you like that?" She knew she was grasping here and hoped that the gorgon couldn't sense the extent of her powers, (which as far as she could tell, were all but nonexistent). She'd only managed to catch Jurid through quick thinking and luck, and with a trap not even she had built. Still, the creature didn't know these things and Heath felt suddenly far too cocky to have stopped herself. She wondered if perhaps some of that millennium old experience Quinton had told her she possessed smoldered now in her expression.

"Not mud," the creature said haltingly, considering the idea with obvious trepidation. "All squishy and wet. . . No, not to mud! Klachilies would not like that."

"Well I don't think I like *you* very much. And I don't think I like this killing of dragons very much either. And saying you want to kill *me* as well. . ? I think you are horrible and mean. I think that perhaps you might be better off as a mud puddle!"

"No, no. Not mud puddle. . !" The gorgon moved from foot to foot, now thoroughly sullen and frightened. The change in the gorgon's diposition had only taken a few instants, but there it was, from terrifying to feeble. Heath thought the creature might even try to run away. "Not squishy little puddle," it moaned. "Little sorceress *very* powerful. Please not kill Klachilies!"

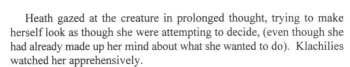

Heath gazed at the creature in prolonged thought, trying to make herself look as though she were attempting to decide, (even though she had already made up her mind about what she wanted to do). Klachilies watched her apprehensively.

"Well. .," she said slowly. "I *do* need somebody to show me how to get to this tea-house tower place. Maybe if you knew the way. . ?"

"Yes! Yes, yes!" it cried, ecstatic. "Yes! Know the way! Will show you! Come with me!"

And with that, the gorgon turned and shambled off, motioning for Heath to follow.

"Come with me! Come, come! Will show you. No mud puddle for me. Klachilies will take you there!"

And so Heath, giving her blessings a quick count, picked her way from the crevice and followed.

King Rillion of Oceansend and the Thief of the Sleeping Wood, (as Rubel had announced himself), were engaged in a discussion of their own. They were talking about the king's daughter.

Rubel, of course, had heard all about how meetings of this sort were supposed to go. —Young suitors going before the fathers of the girls they loved to be tested and intimidated, and fathers miserable about their daughters going away.

Rubel had certainly entertained quivery and exciting thoughts of love concerning Katara, and the king guessed it, having once been a boy himself. This meeting, however, was very different and both of them knew that as well. There was no time for antler locking and firm handshakes. Not in the heart of a dragon's dream. Here, the king and Rubel, despite the fact that neither of them were particularly eloquent or dire in their regular lives, found themselves invested at that moment with an uncommon clarity and seriousness of mind which comes with the realization that one is rising to an important occasion.

"Katara did not speak to me of a thief swearing himself to her," the king said. "When did this occur?"

"Four years ago. We agreed at the time not to speak of it. We felt it concerned only ourselves."

"And who are you? How did you come to know my daughter? I do not recognize you from the court or palace ways."

"I am not from your courts," Rubel told him. "Nor from the palace. I met your daughter in the Sleeping Wood. On the day you sent both she and the prince to search for your crown. On the day of the contest."

"That day. . !" The king's eyes widened.

"At the time I was living in the forest, and I saw you the night before when you hid the crown in an old tree. And I was watching when a witch followed you. And I also saw the prince following *her*. He watched and then took the crown and hid it somewhere so that only *he* would know where it was. —So that he could get it himself the next morning and win the day by cheating. Except I stole all of these schemes out from under the three of you. I took the crown from where Kangar had hidden it and kept it for myself."

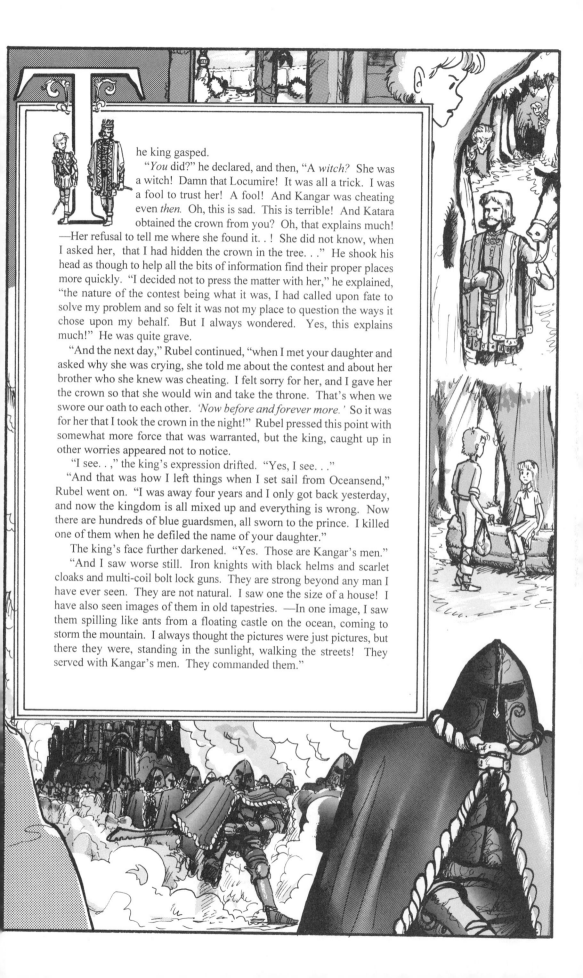

he king gasped.

"*You* did?" he declared, and then, "A *witch?* She was a witch! Damn that Locumire! It was all a trick. I was a fool to trust her! A fool! And Kangar was cheating even *then*. Oh, this is sad. This is terrible! And Katara obtained the crown from you? Oh, that explains much! —Her refusal to tell me where she found it. . ! She did not know, when I asked her, that I had hidden the crown in the tree. . ." He shook his head as though to help all the bits of information find their proper places more quickly. "I decided not to press the matter with her," he explained, "the nature of the contest being what it was, I had called upon fate to solve my problem and so felt it was not my place to question the ways it chose upon my behalf. But I always wondered. Yes, this explains much!" He was quite grave.

"And the next day," Rubel continued, "when I met your daughter and asked why she was crying, she told me about the contest and about her brother who she knew was cheating. I felt sorry for her, and I gave her the crown so that she would win and take the throne. That's when we swore our oath to each other. *'Now before and forever more.'* So it was for her that I took the crown in the night!" Rubel pressed this point with somewhat more force that was warranted, but the king, caught up in other worries appeared not to notice.

"I see. . ," the king's expression drifted. "Yes, I see. . ."

"And that was how I left things when I set sail from Oceansend," Rubel went on. "I was away four years and I only got back yesterday, and now the kingdom is all mixed up and everything is wrong. Now there are hundreds of blue guardsmen, all sworn to the prince. I killed one of them when he defiled the name of your daughter."

The king's face further darkened. "Yes. Those are Kangar's men."

"And I saw worse still. Iron knights with black helms and scarlet cloaks and multi-coil bolt lock guns. They are strong beyond any man I have ever seen. They are not natural. I saw one the size of a house! I have also seen images of them in old tapestries. —In one image, I saw them spilling like ants from a floating castle on the ocean, coming to storm the mountain. I always thought the pictures were just pictures, but there they were, standing in the sunlight, walking the streets! They served with Kangar's men. They commanded them."

he king's face now blanched and he looked at Rubel with a frightful gaze.

"Not the Lamp Knights! It cannot be! My son has not found the words to bring those horrors to life? This is foul! It is black magic which has poisoned my son's heart! Black magic! This explains many things! Go on. Tell me what else you saw!"

"It gets worse," Rubel said. "There was a spell on the palace. A strong one. —After I heard the rumours about your daughter, I went to see if I could find her, and if not her then to find you so that we could have this very discussion. But when I went, I found your palace under a spell. The gate opened up to me all by itself, and the streets and ways of the palace were completely empty. I walked unchallenged into the very heart of the castle; all the way up to your chambers and right next to your bed side. I saw you lying there! You were asleep, I suppose, while your spirit was trapped here. Then the spell ended. It ended when I met a challenge meant especially for me."

"A challenge?" the king asked. "In my chamber?"

Rubel frowned in thought and then continued.

"I know this lady. . ," he explained, "A black-magic sorceress. —She's the one who brought me here. And she was also the one who opened up the palace drawbridge and led me to your chambers. And when she'd done all of that, I met her challenge for my soul and wouldn't succumb to her, so the spell she was using came loose from me and the palace was filled again with people. With prince Kangar's guardsmen and the Iron Knights."

The king looked past him in thought. "This black-magic sorceress," he said, "Was this the witch, Locumire?"

"No," Rubel shook his head. "She is somebody else. She is much more powerful than a witch. She is almost a goddess. She does not die."

"So *she* is the enemy? She is the cause of it all? I know the one! She has visited the other kings trapped here! I didn't know she existed in the waking world as well!"

"She's real, alright," Rubel assured him. "But I don't think she's the one behind everything. She brought me here because she wanted to *help*. I don't want to fight her if I don't have to. I think there's a chance of her being a friend."

T he king squinted and thought for a long moment.

"You are certain of this?" he asked. "Sorcery is an art of tricks. One can never be too careful when it comes to women of magic. Helpless or seductive, a sorceress can appear as many things to gain ends you might never even fathom!"

"I know, but the worst of her tricks play on the heart and soul; hers and mine. But I think she's fond of me, and I think it's real. It's not easy to confuse a thief in matters of that sort. When I look into her eyes, I can tell that she is good and beautiful inside. —She's still very dangerous to be sure, but I think I want to make that *my* concern. Besides, I don't think anyone else has the power to confront her. She commands terrible magic. Your men would not stand a chance against her!"

"And you would?"

"Yes." Rubel thought about this and then felt certain. "Yes."

"Very well," the king frowned. "But you must know that as king, I will leave this matter in your hands only so long as it does not spill over into mine. If she needs to be slain, an attempt must be made and I will make it, no matter how capable you judge my forces. I only hope that you will not find yourself beguiled if such a time should come. You *or* me. She is beautiful on the outside as well?"

"Very. But I will not be beguiled. I am a thief."

"You are also very young."

"I know. But I can see clearly the ways of things beyond what others can. I have been trained by a wizard. And I am already sworn to a girl. To Katara."

The king nodded gravely. "And what of my men? My personal guard? Did you see them in the palace as well? Did they face this sorceress"

"No. They were there, but she did not make herself known to them. They *did* see me. I tried to run, but they caught me. —And there was a battle between them and prince Kangar's men. They all seemed to know that I was the princess's thief, and Kangar's soldiers wanted to take me but your Majesty Guard would not allow it. I was sorely wounded from a fight in the city; I carried the very wound which eventually brought me here. If I hadn't been hurt though, I probably would have gotten away. But I didn't and battle broke out."

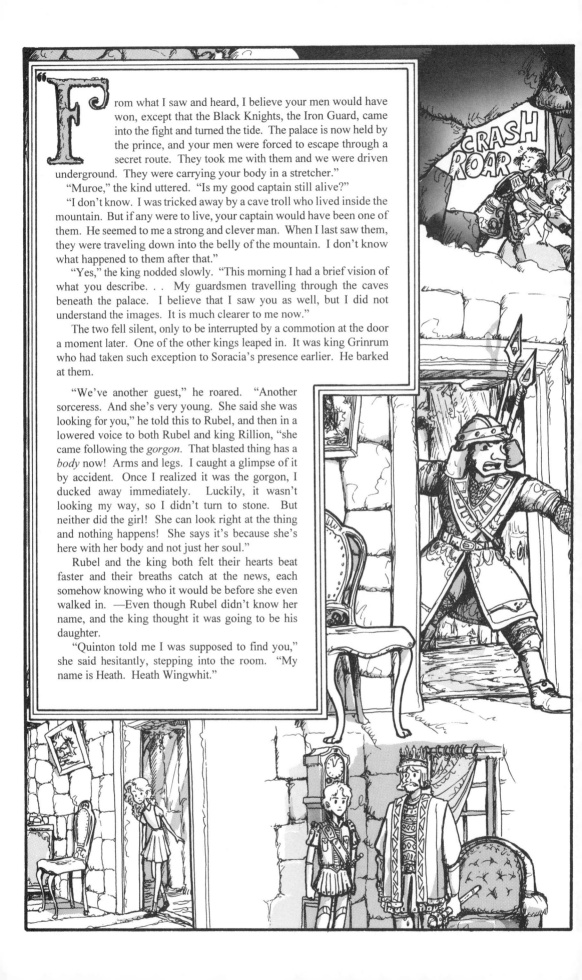

"From what I saw and heard, I believe your men would have won, except that the Black Knights, the Iron Guard, came into the fight and turned the tide. The palace is now held by the prince, and your men were forced to escape through a secret route. They took me with them and we were driven underground. They were carrying your body in a stretcher."

"Muroe," the kind uttered. "Is my good captain still alive?"

"I don't know. I was tricked away by a cave troll who lived inside the mountain. But if any were to live, your captain would have been one of them. He seemed to me a strong and clever man. When I last saw them, they were traveling down into the belly of the mountain. I don't know what happened to them after that."

"Yes," the king nodded slowly. "This morning I had a brief vision of what you describe. . . My guardsmen travelling through the caves beneath the palace. I believe that I saw you as well, but I did not understand the images. It is much clearer to me now."

The two fell silent, only to be interrupted by a commotion at the door a moment later. One of the other kings leaped in. It was king Grinrum who had taken such exception to Soracia's presence earlier. He barked at them.

"We've another guest," he roared. "Another sorceress. And she's very young. She said she was looking for you," he told this to Rubel, and then in a lowered voice to both Rubel and king Rillion, "she came following the *gorgon*. That blasted thing has a *body* now! Arms and legs. I caught a glimpse of it by accident. Once I realized it was the gorgon, I ducked away immediately. Luckily, it wasn't looking my way, so I didn't turn to stone. But neither did the girl! She can look right at the thing and nothing happens! She says it's because she's here with her body and not just her soul."

Rubel and the king both felt their hearts beat faster and their breaths catch at the news, each somehow knowing who it would be before she even walked in. —Even though Rubel didn't know her name, and the king thought it was going to be his daughter.

"Quinton told me I was supposed to find you," she said hesitantly, stepping into the room. "My name is Heath. Heath Wingwhit."

Chapter 2

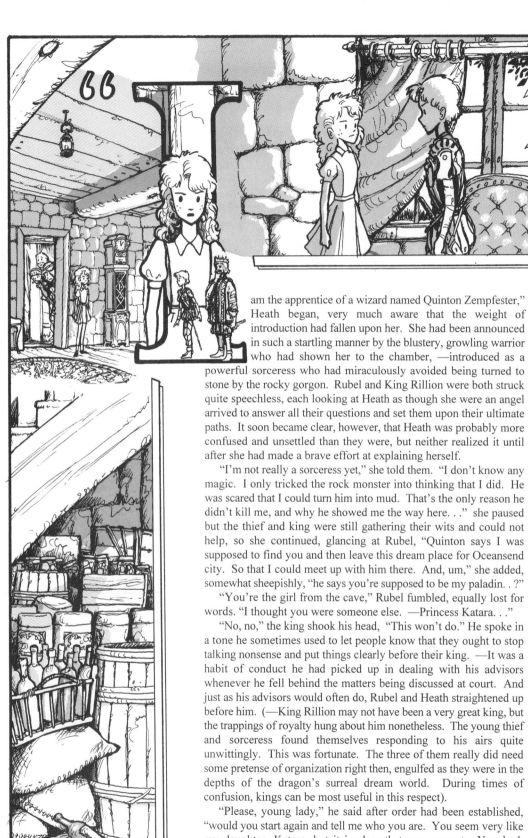

"I am the apprentice of a wizard named Quinton Zempfester," Heath began, very much aware that the weight of introduction had fallen upon her. She had been announced in such a startling manner by the blustery, growling warrior who had shown her to the chamber, —introduced as a powerful sorceress who had miraculously avoided being turned to stone by the rocky gorgon. Rubel and King Rillion were both struck quite speechless, each looking at Heath as though she were an angel arrived to answer all their questions and set them upon their ultimate paths. It soon became clear, however, that Heath was probably more confused and unsettled than they were, but neither realized it until after she had made a brave effort at explaining herself.

"I'm not really a sorceress yet," she told them. "I don't know any magic. I only tricked the rock monster into thinking that I did. He was scared that I could turn him into mud. That's the only reason he didn't kill me, and why he showed me the way here. . ." she paused but the thief and king were still gathering their wits and could not help, so she continued, glancing at Rubel, "Quinton says I was supposed to find you and then leave this dream place for Oceansend city. So that I could meet up with him there. And, um," she added, somewhat sheepishly, "he says you're supposed to be my paladin. . ?"

"You're the girl from the cave," Rubel fumbled, equally lost for words. "I thought you were someone else. —Princess Katara. . ."

"No, no," the king shook his head, "This won't do." He spoke in a tone he sometimes used to let people know that they ought to stop talking nonsense and put things clearly before their king. —It was a habit of conduct he had picked up in dealing with his advisors whenever he fell behind the matters being discussed at court. And just as his advisors would often do, Rubel and Heath straightened up before him. (—King Rillion may not have been a very great king, but the trappings of royalty hung about him nonetheless. The young thief and sorceress found themselves responding to his airs quite unwittingly. This was fortunate. The three of them really did need some pretense of organization right then, engulfed as they were in the depths of the dragon's surreal dream world. During times of confusion, kings can be most useful in this respect).

"Please, young lady," he said after order had been established, "would you start again and tell me who you are. You seem very like my daughter, Katara, but it is clear that you are not. You look different for a start; younger and more freckly. And Katara, I know is lost somewhere back home. But there is something quite unmistakable. . . Please, if you would, explain who you are and where you are from. Take your time. There is no rush."

Heath took a long breath and did as King Rillion asked, repeating her name and then telling the king about her home in Millbrook. King Rillion listened to her intently, asking many questions. 'Who was in power?' 'Were the desert kingdoms still our enemies?' and 'Did the Raspberry Valleys still have raspberries growing in them?'

Heath answered everything he asked as best she could, and the king squinted in thought and nodded encouragingly. He appeared particularly interested in what Quinton had written to her in the letter she found waiting upon her arrival in the dream garden. After several more questions, he let her go quiet, then both she and Rubel watched him, as though he were a doctor considering his prognosis.

"Yes," he pondered slowly. "Yes. I would place you in the reign of King Geof the Third. The battles of Millbrook and Shoals are somewhat obscure, but I do know them from my history lessons as a boy. —Though I don't recall magic or witchery being the cause of those incidents! Locumire, however, I most certainly *do* remember. The woman looked old to me, but a *thousand* years! That's something. That's magic, to be certain!" He rose grimly before Heath. "You are from a thousand years in my past, young Miss Wingwhit. A *thousand years*, round about as I can tell!"

Rubel looked at Heath with awe, and she looked back at him, helpless. The king nodded again.

"I have spoken with the other kings trapped here in this tower," he explained. "They are from all across history and time; times before mine. I knew several of their names from my studies when I was young. They lived and died long ago, and yet they are here, trapped in this mysterious place. —We have discussed our situation at length, and we have concluded that this world is a sort of holding well for souls. The dream of a dragon! It is all very mysterious.

"Beyond that, the ultimate reason for our being here is unclear. All we are certain of is that time moves in strange ways and that this tower and this whole dream land exists separately from the flow of events in the waking world. It may seem very strange," Rillion said prophetically, "but it is no surprise to me that you, Miss Wingwhit, are from a different period in history." He concluded this testimony with an important looking raise of his forehead, also characteristic of his royal trappings.

Oh," Heath said, numbed by a mixture of wonder and misery which troubled her senses in a sea-sick sort of way. —Wonder at the adventurous and magical aspect of it all, but misery at having it quite confirmed by nothing less than a king that she was indeed very lost. All the king's questions about Millbrook caused everything she loved to well up clear and potent in her mind; things which had been shuffled to the back of her thoughts during all the danger and running about involved in getting there.

Heath found herself sorely missing Finnly and her cousin Davin. —Friends, she realized, she would likely never see again; friends she really could have used at her side right then. A bleak worm of despair began to twist its way through her heart as all of this settled upon her. With a great effort, she roused herself to push it away. 'Later,' she told herself. The events happening here and now were very important and if she let herself dwell upon sad things she would certainly start to cry, and this was neither the time nor the place for that.

"But what I do not understand," the king went on, "is why you seem so much like my daughter. And if I read our young thief's expression correctly, he wonders this very thing as well. You do look so like my dear Katara."

Heath looked between the two of them, her face pale, and she forced herself to think.

"Well. . ," she began, her voice heavy and wrong in her throat, "I know I'm not your daughter, sir. —Um, your highness. . . I know because I can still sort of remember what my dad was like. He was very different from you. He wasn't a king, anyway. But maybe I remind you of your daughter because I'm. . . That is, after I left Millbrook. . ," she stopped and tried to gather her thoughts.

With all the sorrow in the world swelling inside of her, she found herself fumbling uselessly with the concepts of time travel and reincarnation. It swirled about in the turbulent ocean of her thoughts, reluctant to be wrapped up in words for any sort of explaining. It did not help matters that Rubel and the king both stood quietly before her, waiting in that agonizingly patient and polite way people have when they are trying, but failing, to let somebody sort out their thoughts. Thus, beneath this final stress, the fragile construct of Heath's resolve spun gently into oblivion.

A tear slipped down her cheek and the cozy upstairs bedroom she had been given for her own swam before her mind's eye. —Given to her by her uncle and aunt; Aunt Emma, warm and beautiful, who had told her it was alright to call her 'Mom.' She felt the burn of embarrassment for crying and fled the room, leaving the king and thief in confusion.

After they found her, and didn't know what to say, they paced about awkwardly while she cried, feeling miserable now themselves as though her tears were their fault. Heath was emotionally exhausted. Not just from this, but from the past three days, which for her had been filled with many powerful events; bullies and fights, and people she loved being hurt or taken away from her. And this whole day, filled with the loss of friends without good-byes, and with hate-filled monsters trying to slay her. And with being lost. Heath was a very strong person, but she was still very young. And even strong people have their limits.

Still, even as she wept, her emotions, like shins or knuckles which had been scraped repeatedly until raw, were sensitive now to *other* forces. Heath was taken with powerful surges of affection for the king. He was a very *good* person, she knew at once; he had a wonderful father-like feel about him as he patted her on the shoulder, something she had missed for many years. And the boy. . , Rubel, she felt as though she had known and trusted him for a very long time as well, as though he *were* her paladin, but this only made her feel more confused. She squeezed her eyes shut, but there was more.

All about her was Cespinarve Rogue; smallest of all the dragons; the one nobody loved. The one who had nonetheless fought the enemy to save every dragon, and indeed, all of Nove. She felt Rogue everywhere about her. And further, she could sense that Rogue felt *her* as well; that the dragon somehow *knew* her and adored her; *treasured* her with a kind of desperation. All of these confused feelings swept through her, making her shiver and sob under the crook of the king's arm; under the arm of the man who would one day be her father, (a thought which seemed all at once both impossible and ridiculous, and which made her laugh a feverish sounding laugh which alarmed the thief and king all the more).

"It's okay," she choked through her tears, seeing their worry. "I'm all right. I'm sorry. I'm all right." She wasn't really, and so cried for a little more, but after a while the intensity of all these many feelings withdrew somewhat, and she was able to take some deep breaths and clear her eyes.

"Better now?" the king asked gently.

She nodded, wiping her cheeks. She took another deep breath. "Quinton told met that I've lived nearly three hundred lives," she explained, "I reincarnate each time into a new body. I can't remember anything from each life, but that's how it works."

Neither the king nor Rubel knew what to say, but they both nodded their heads, each relieved to see that she had returned to herself. She went on.

So what I probably am is the same *person* as your daughter," she explained to the king, "but from *before* she was born." She watched them to see if they understood, and then added, recalling her last hurried conversation with the wizard, "Quinton also said I was going to have a *double* where I was going. He probably meant your daughter." She decided to leave out the part about her possibly going mad as a result, and wondered briefly if this possibility might not apply to Katara as well.

The king made a number of intent expressions, and then replied, "If souls are born over and over again, as some suggest they are. . . And if yours has lived many lives before this one, then perhaps it is possible. . ?"

"I think that's how it is," she said.

"It is very peculiar, though," the king sighed. "Most strange. You have all the airs of my Katara about you. I can see her expression in your face. It is most peculiar."

"And if you are Katara's spirit. . ," Rubel spoke up, "that is, if she is *yours*, then that means I must be your thief."

"But *why?*" Heath asked. "Quinton said you were my paladin, but I don't understand why. Are you Katara's knight?".

"No," Rubel shook his head. "I am her *thief*. Anything she needs or wants me to do, I will do, so long as I am able. All she has to do is wish it. We swore an oath together when I first met her in the woods. I swore that I would be her thief, and that she would be my lady, *'Now before and forever more.'* And she cut a little lock from her hair and tied a ribbon bow around it and gave it to me to seal our promise."

"Ohh. .," Heath said quietly, struck by Rubel's tone and by the burn in his eyes, for he believed strongly in these sorts of things. "You fell in love with her. . ?" she asked.

"Um," Rubel stopped at this and cautiously debated over how he ought to answer. "Yes," he decided, casting a furtive glance at the king who watched him back. I'd give my life for her if I had to."

Heath caught her breath as another question struck her;

'Oh!' she thought. *'But if they fell in love with each other, then what does that mean? If I have the same soul as her, and I do, for she lies in my future, then will I fall in love with this boy too? Why, it means we are destined. Destined! It must be so!'* She swallowed on this hard and her face felt hot and she was lost in a panic as these ideas flew like sparrows. It was too much! *Too much,* her mind begged.

ubel carried on, standing proudly as he spoke, "Since you're Katara from before, I am sworn to you as well. Quinton was right. I will be yours however you might need me! I will be your thief!"

"Oh," Heath managed to squeak, feeling herself blush furiously and her tears threaten for a precarious moment to start again, "Um. . . Yes, I suppose so." She could not look at him. It was all she could do to stare fixedly at the laces of the king's boots. The king saw this and understood.

"Please, would you tell me more about this Quinton fellow?" he asked. "He came visiting this tower some time ago and he put up that wall you see yonder, but again I had not yet arrived here at that point. He explained very little about himself to the other kings. He said he'd look after us later, but has not returned since." He paused and then added, "I think that perhaps you two know far more than anybody in this matter."

Heath gushed at the chance. Between Rubel and she, they explained what they knew about Quinton, learning several pieces from each other in the process, and informing the king of much.

"I was hoping when things are sorted out," Rubel finished, "and I found Katara, that she could find a place for Quinton in your courts. I thought a wizard could be useful to a king in many ways, and the tower he lives in now is all leaky with a big hole in the ceiling."

"He does sound like a most resourceful chap," the king observed. "But I must say I am surprised he was living under my nose the whole time without my knowing." He shook his head and breathed through his moustache. "But that's the way of wizards, I suppose, isn't it?"

The two nodded.

But I still have to go find him," Rubel said with a frown. "When I do, I'll bring him back. I want to ask him if he can help find my grandfather who was lost at sea. —And I'll have him heal you from the magical sleep you're in. That way you'll wake back up in Oceansend and can deal with your son. I can help you with that, too," he added. "But before Kangar, I first want to find Katara."

Rillion nodded gravely. "Yes. She needs to be found."

They talked further, this time about the Shadow Lady. Rubel and Rillion were stunned to learn that Heath and Soracia were sisters. Heath watched them with apprehension after she divulged this intelligence; the king appeared troubled and confused, but little more. —Perhaps because he had never met Soracia and she hadn't tried to cut him in two as she had with Heath. Rubel, however, practically choked over the news.

"You're her *sister?*" he exclaimed. "Wow! Well! *That* certainly explains some things! I always wondered how Katara's lock of hair could be so useful against a sorceress like the Shadow Lady! —If they were *sisters."* His mind raced. "And in the cave. . . All those ghosts. . !"

"I see. .," the king said distantly before regaining himself. He shook his head. "But you say you are wounded?" he asked Rubel. "How badly?"

Rubel frowned again and looked thoughtful. "Right now. . ? Very badly," he admitted. "My body is lying in an alleyway. I hope the bleeding isn't too bad. I'm sort of hoping the wound swelled up and blocked it off like Quinton said. . ."

He didn't look very hopeful. Heath bit her lip, bewildered.

"You're hurt?" she asked.

"In my side. I was shot."

Rubel and the king explained to her what they knew of the nature of the Dream Garden. Heath was disturbed to learn that the king and Rubel, to travel here from the waking world, had both been poisoned and were dying.

Their discussion quickly turned to the matter of what they ought to do next. Rubel, reminded of the urgency of his position, was not at all anxious to extend his visit. There was something odd about this dream world which made it easy to forget oneself, and realizing this made him even more agitated. He looked over to Heath and found her staring back at him fixedly. She was stiff and straight in her chair, her face a picture of tension.

"I think we ought to get going very soon," she said.

Both the king and Rubel agreed. They talked and planned for a little while more, but then set about leaving.

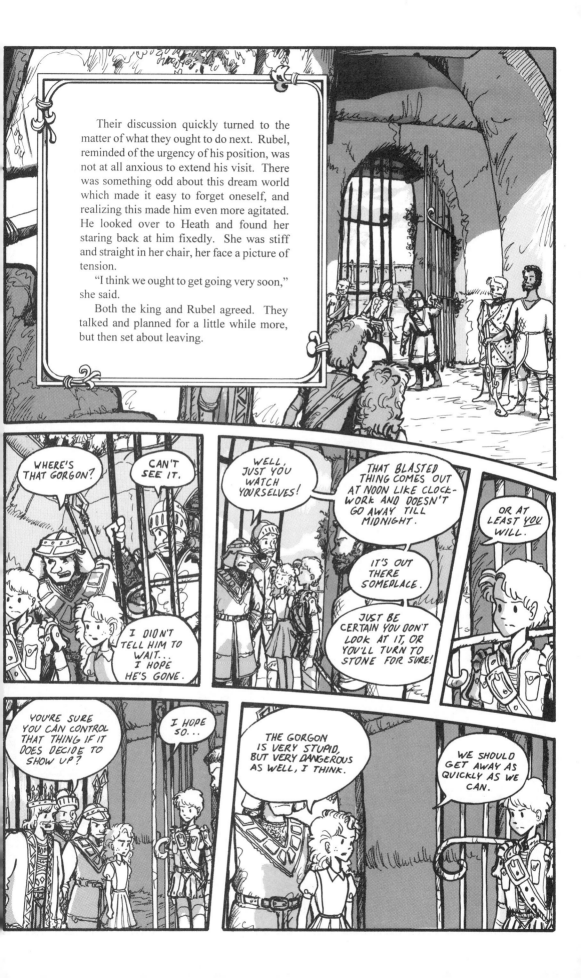

IT'S CESPINARVE ROGUE!

HE'S HELPING US!

COME ON! LET'S GET OUT OF HERE!

I KNEW HE WASN'T EVIL!

I KNEW IT!

I DON'T THINK THE GORGON IS THE SORT OF MONSTER THAT STAYS DEAD ONCE YOU KILL IT.

WE HAVE TO BE QUICK!

HERE IT IS!

THE WAY OUT!

I HAVE TO GO THROUGH THE BUSHES THE WAY I CAME IN, BUT YOU HAVE TO GO THROUGH THE WATER.

STAND BACK!

THERE'S SQUID MONSTERS IN THESE THINGS!

NO! YOU DON'T HAVE TO!

UNDERSTAND? CESPINARVE IS HELPING US! THERE WON'T BE A SQUID MONSTER.

HE WOULDN'T PUT ONE THERE.

WHAT ARE YOU TALKING ABOUT?!

HE'S A DRAGON! DRAGONS ARE SELFISH AND CRUEL. OF COURSE HE'LL PUT ONE THERE!

NOT CESPINARVE!

HE ONLY DOES MEAN THINGS BECAUSE NOBODY LOVES HIM. --BUT THAT DOESN'T MAKE HIM EVIL!

YES IT DOES!

DRAGONS ARE ALL EVIL!

NO THEY'RE NOT! --DRAGONS ARE IMPORTANT!

BUT THE OTHER DRAGONS ARE MEAN TO HIM. --I DON'T THINK HE'S EVER HAD A FRIEND.

I THINK I'M THE ONLY ONE WHO DOESN'T HATE HIM!

SO WHY WOULD HE TRY TO KEEP ME TRAPPED HERE IN HIS GARDEN?

OOOOO...

AAARGH

Chapter 3

BOTH OF YOU!!

CUT IT OUT!!

CESPINARVE! LEAVE HIM ALONE!

I CAN'T STAY HERE! WE HAVE TO GO!

I KNOW YOU'RE LONELY, BUT I CAN'T STAY! PLEASE DON'T MAKE ME!

I'LL COME BACK.

--I PROMISE!

TO TAKE AWAY THE KINGS AND LEAVE ME!

NO. --TO TAKE AWAY THE GORGON TOO!

AND THEN YOU CAN WAKE UP. --AND THE OTHER DRAGONS WILL BE GRATEFUL TO YOU FOR FIGHTING THE GORGON! --FROM WHEN YOU FOUGHT HIM BEFORE. --AND SAVED ALL OF THEM!

HATE THEM, HEATH..! HATE THEM...

PLEASE CESPINARVE. I CAN'T STAY.

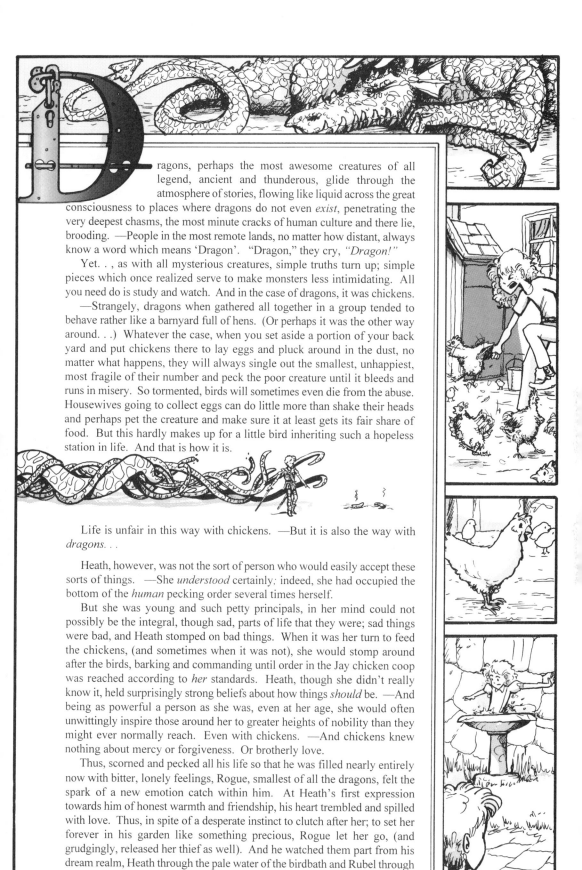

Dragons, perhaps the most awesome creatures of all legend, ancient and thunderous, glide through the atmosphere of stories, flowing like liquid across the great consciousness to places where dragons do not even *exist*, penetrating the very deepest chasms, the most minute cracks of human culture and there lie, brooding. —People in the most remote lands, no matter how distant, always know a word which means 'Dragon'. "Dragon," they cry, *"Dragon!"*

Yet. ., as with all mysterious creatures, simple truths turn up; simple pieces which once realized serve to make monsters less intimidating. All you need do is study and watch. And in the case of dragons, it was chickens.

—Strangely, dragons when gathered all together in a group tended to behave rather like a barnyard full of hens. (Or perhaps it was the other way around. . .) Whatever the case, when you set aside a portion of your back yard and put chickens there to lay eggs and pluck around in the dust, no matter what happens, they will always single out the smallest, unhappiest, most fragile of their number and peck the poor creature until it bleeds and runs in misery. So tormented, birds will sometimes even die from the abuse. Housewives going to collect eggs can do little more than shake their heads and perhaps pet the creature and make sure it at least gets its fair share of food. But this hardly makes up for a little bird inheriting such a hopeless station in life. And that is how it is.

Life is unfair in this way with chickens. —But it is also the way with *dragons. . .*

Heath, however, was not the sort of person who would easily accept these sorts of things. —She *understood* certainly; indeed, she had occupied the bottom of the *human* pecking order several times herself.

But she was young and such petty principals, in her mind could not possibly be the integral, though sad, parts of life that they were; sad things were bad, and Heath stomped on bad things. When it was her turn to feed the chickens, (and sometimes when it was not), she would stomp around after the birds, barking and commanding until order in the Jay chicken coop was reached according to *her* standards. Heath, though she didn't really know it, held surprisingly strong beliefs about how things *should* be. —And being as powerful a person as she was, even at her age, she would often unwittingly inspire those around her to greater heights of nobility than they might ever normally reach. Even with chickens. —And chickens knew nothing about mercy or forgiveness. Or brotherly love.

Thus, scorned and pecked all his life so that he was filled nearly entirely now with bitter, lonely feelings, Rogue, smallest of all the dragons, felt the spark of a new emotion catch within him. At Heath's first expression towards him of honest warmth and friendship, his heart trembled and spilled with love. Thus, in spite of a desperate instinct to clutch after her; to set her forever in his garden like something precious, Rogue let her go, (and grudgingly, released her thief as well). And he watched them part from his dream realm, Heath through the pale water of the birdbath and Rubel through the undergrowth where the thief had first entered. And then, like the lords locked away in King's Crossing, Rogue settled down to wait on her return.

HUU

UGGG

MOANN...

RUBEL?

SPLASH

WAA!

PHOO

PUFF
PUFF

I DON'T KNOW.
--A PRETTY
LONG TIME.

IT'S THAT STUPID QUINTON AND HIS DUMB STORIES!

JAQUES QUICK WASN'T EVEN REAL, I BET!

AND IF HE WAS, I BET HE DIED FOLLOWING QUINTON'S STUPID ADVICE!

DO YOU THINK YOU CAN FIX HIM BEFORE HE DIES?

I REALLY DON'T WANT HIM TO DIE.

I DON'T KNOW.

WE HAVE TO GET HIM TO A DOCTOR!

MAYBE YOU SHOULD USE YOUR MAGIC?

WELL, ACTUALLY, I DON'T REALLY...

WHAT?

OH GREAT.

RUBEL GOT ANOTHER SORCERESS WHO DOESN'T KNOW ANY MAGIC.

SORRY...

I JUST STARTED LEARNING A FEW DAYS AGO...

OH.

WHAT ARE WE GOING TO DO?

WELL,

SHE MARRIED THE BAKER'S SON.
--HE WAS ONE OF OUR ENEMIES.

OH.

WILL SHE HELP, DO YOU THINK?

I DON'T KNOW.
--I'M NOT SURPRISED SHE TURNED TRAITOR.

BUT HER MOM'S STILL NICE.
-SHE STILL LIKES RUBEL.

SHOULD WE GO TO HER, DO YOU THINK?

YES!
WE SHOULD GO!

YEAH!
MAYBE SHE KNOWS A DOCTOR OR SOMEBODY.

COME ON!

IT'S NOT VERY FAR.

THAT'S THE PLACE?

YEAH.

NUMBER FOURTEEN.

DON'T YOU HAVE ANY POCKETS OR ANYTHING?

I HAVE TO HIDE!

IF PEOPLE SEE ME TOO MUCH, THEY'LL TIE YOU TO A POST AND SET YOU ON FIRE!

EEAH..! SET ME ON FIRE?

I DON'T WANT THAT!

NO KIDDING.

BUT I DON'T **HAVE** ANY POCKETS.

BUMMER.

YOU WAIT HERE. --I'LL GO BANG ON THE DOOR.

14

BANG BANG

SO THERE'S AN EMERGENCY, IS THERE?

YES MA'AM.

MMM...

YOU'RE FILTHY.

HORRIBLY FILTHY!

AND DAMP!

MIND YOU STAY IN THE HALL THERE!

DON'T GET MUCK ON THE RUG!

NO MA'AM!

SORRY.

WHAT IS YOUR NAME, GIRL?

UM, HEATH.

HEATH WINGWHIT, MA'AM.

YOU'RE RATHER *YOUNG* TO BE RUNNING ABOUT WITH A BOY LIKE RUBEL, AREN'T YOU?

YOU'D DO WELL TO STAY AWAY FROM HIM!

WHO ARE YOUR PARENTS?

--I DON'T KNOW ANY WINGWHITS.

UM...

WHAT PART OF THE CITY ARE YOU FROM?

YOU LIVE IN THE *POORER* DISTRICT, DO YOU?

ER...

SPEAK UP, GIRL.

UM...,

YES?

HMM...

I CAN'T SAY I'M TERRIBLY SURPRISED.

SO WHAT HAPPENED TO THAT BOY?

WHAT'S THE EMERGENCY?

HE'S HURT.

I GATHERED THAT MUCH ON MY OWN.. --HOW DID HE GET HURT?

UM... HE GOT **SHOT**...

OH **DID** HE?

IN HIS SIDE.

YES.

HUM! UP TO NO GOOD, THEN, WAS HE?

I DIDN'T SEE IT HAPPEN...

WELL THAT'S THE ONLY WAY PEOPLE COME TO GET SHOT IN **MY** KNOWLEDGE!

SERVES HIM RIGHT!

FILTHY BOYS WHO CALL TROUBLE DOWN UPON THEMSELVES DON'T **DESERVE** HELP FROM GOOD YOUNG MEN LIKE **SMITH ROBINS!**

PSST! HEATH!

QUICK!

WHAT IS IT?

IT'S A **SOLDIER!**

SHE'S BRINGING BACK A **SOLDIER!**

HE CAN'T FIND OUT ABOUT RUBEL!

IF HE DOES, THEY'LL **KILL** HIM!

RUBEL'S NOT STRONG ENOUGH TO FIGHT!

AND HOW DID THIS BOY COME TO GET HURT, MRS. PORTER?

I DON'T KNOW, BUT IT'S QUITE URGENT!

THIS IS **BAD!** YOU HAVE TO GET RID OF HIM!

THERE SHE IS!

OH, SWEETHEART! YOU LOOK TERRIBLE!

DON'T WORRY, **SMITH ROBINS** WILL HELP.

COME ON! WE HAVE TO GO!

PERHAPS I OUGHT TO CALL UP SOME OF THE OTHER MEN TO HELP.

WOULD THEY DO THAT? --THAT WOULD BE AN EXCELLENT IDEA.

WHICH WAY IS IT, HONEY?

THIS WAY, DOWN HERE.

BUT, UM..,

I DON'T THINK WE NEED ANY EXTRA HELP.

NO, REALLY, --IT'S NO PROBLEM.

HEY!

YOU THERE!

ROBINS! HO THERE!

WHERE HAVE YOU BEEN? --THERE'S A SEARCH ON!

WHAT HAVE YOU GOT THERE?

THERE'S PLENTY OF OTHERS ABOUT. PUT YOUR DUTY ASIDE FOR A MOMENT.

THIS LITTLE GIRL NEEDS OUR HELP!

ONE OF HER YOUNG FRIENDS HAS BEEN INJURED!

A YOUNG BOY HAS BEEN BADLY HURT!

WE NEED A DOCTOR!

HO! THAT'S SERIOUS!

I'LL GO RUN FOR A DOCTOR!

DON'T WORRY! WE'LL SET THINGS STRAIGHT!

JUST SHOW US WHERE HE IS. --WE'LL SEE THAT HE GETS ATTENTION!

ERG...

COME ON!

WHAT'S WRONG WITH YOUR FRIEND?

WHAT HAPPENED?

HE WAS HURT. HE'S BLEEDING VERY BADLY!

BLEEDING?!

HOW OLD IS THIS BOY? --WHAT DOES HE LOOK LIKE?

DOES HE HAVE DIRTY-BLOND HAIR?

WHY? WHAT'S THE MATTER?

YES! WHAT'S GOING ON?

WHERE HAVE YOU BEEN?

THERE'S A SEARCH ON!

PRINCESS KATARA HAS A THIEF, AND SHE SENT HIM TO TOWN TO CREATE MISCHIEF!

HE'S KILLED AT LEAST A DOZEN OF OUR MEN!

THE PRINCESS IS DECLARING WAR ON THE WHOLE CITY!!

HER THIEF STORMED THE PALACE AND THE MAJESTY GUARD ROSE UP ON HIS ORDERS AND FOLLOWED HIM INTO BATTLE!

HE WENT TO ASSASSINATE THE PRINCE!

MY GOOOONESS!

COME NOW!

YOU STUMBLED ACROSS HIM AND FELT SORRY FOR HIM, DID YOU?

LYING THERE HURT, AND YOU WANTED TO RUN FOR HELP? THAT'S QUITE NATURAL.

YOU'RE ONLY VERY YOUNG, AND YOU DON'T KNOW ANY BETTER.

BUT YOU MUST LEAVE THINGS UP TO US.

YOU LOVE YOUR PRINCE, DON'T YOU?

I AM NOT SHOWING YOU WHERE HE IS!

HERE!

THERE'S A TRAIL OF BLOOD!

IN HERE!

IN THIS ALLEY WAY!

NO! LEAVE HIM ALONE!

WHERE IS HE?

HE'S GONE!

Chapter 4

ubel was free. In the moments before Heath and the prince guard arrived, (one wishing to rescue him, the other devising violence), the boy lay in a pool of his own blood, barely aware of himself or his surroundings, but that finally, was all. Earlier, there had been vile poison coursing his veins and crafty magic confusing his body and mind, but they had spent themselves upon the dream journey he had undertaken and the spellwork necessary to send him there, so at long last, he was free. —Though, he was also used up and mostly dead, and actually, the issue of freedom had become a rather questionable subject as well. . .

Promises, promises. . .

Thieves like Rubel and McGi were bound by certain rules. Once sworn, as Rubel was to Katara, (and in a round about way, to Heath as well), a thief was meant to follow every wish of the girl he was sworn to. The problem now was that the Shadow Lady had a hold on him too, though it was not a simple or whole thing. It was complicated. Rubel had offered no solemn oaths to her, nor had she asked for any. But he was still a thief, and while he knew well to fear her, Soracia, in a confusing sort of way was also somebody he cared about. Indeed! His relationship with her was not an easy one to understand at all. At some point, it had become grown up and subtle.

Rubel, however, while he was a thoughtful and compassionate boy, was still a dreamer, and dreamers believe in noble ideals and in marching boldly on and in fighting for a friend no matter what, so it didn't occur to him to worry a great deal.

Actually, right then he wasn't worrying a great deal about anything at all, on account of his being barely conscious and nearly dead. Indeed, it seemed that everybody *but* Rubel was aware of his current situation. The *prince* knew, (or at least his guardsmen did), and they rushed to hunt him down, their sword palms itching. Heath and Mrs. Porter knew, and were anxious to rescue him.

And, of course, little Varkias knew. . .

RUBEL!

YOU HAVE TO GET UP!

THAT GIRL YOU BROUGHT BACK MADE A MISTAKE!

SHE'S BRINGING BACK SOLDIERS!

WHA-?

OPEN UP!

NO!

-- ONLY IF YOU GIVE ME BACK THE LANTERN!

WHAT LANTERN!

OPEN THIS STUPID ROCK!

THE LANTERN YOUR THIEF TOOK FROM ME!

HEY, RUBEL.

HAVE YOU GOT SOME KIND OF LANTERN?

GROAN...

NO!

I'M NOT OPENING UP UNLESS YOU GIVE BACK MY LANTERN!

NO!

NO! IT'S NOT YOURS!

RUBEL!

IT IS TOO, MINE!

YOU STOLE IT!

NO IT'S NOT!

IT WAS GIVEN TO ME AND THEN I GAVE IT TO MY FRIEND, SARA BLUE, ON HER BIRTHDAY!

YOU'RE THE ONE WHO STOLE IT FROM HER!!

SO?!

FINDERS, KEEPERS, LOSERS, WEEPERS!

AND ANYWAY, YOU'RE NOT COMING DOWN HERE UNLESS YOU GIVE IT BACK!

YEAH?

WELL, THERE'S **SOLDIERS** GOING TO BE COMING ANY MOMENT, AND I DON'T CARE WHAT DEALS YOU MIGHT HAVE MADE WITH THE IRON GUARD! --THESE ARE **HUMAN** SOLDIERS!

AND WHEN I TELL THEM THERE'S A **SECRET TUNNEL** DOWN THERE, AND A **TROLL**, THEY'LL TEAR UP THE WHOLE STREET AND THEY'LL FIND ALL YOUR TUNNELS AND THEY'LL HUNT YOU DOWN!

SOLDIERS **HATE** TROLLS!

NOW OPEN UP!

THEY WON'T BELIEVE YOU!

HUMANS **NEVER** BELIEVE!

AND THIS STONE LOCKS FROM DOWN HERE!

ARGH! THEY'RE COMING!

WELL, IF THEY COME AND FIND ME, THEY'LL TAKE THE **LAMP** AND THEN IT'LL BE GONE FOREVER!

!!

SIMPER

GIVE IT BACK!

THEY'RE COMING WITH US!

I WANT TO KNOW HOW THESE TWO CAME TO BE SUCH GOOD FRIENDS WITH THAT **THIEF!**

WHAT?

DON'T BE RIDICULOUS!

WE'RE NOT GOING ANYWHERE!

MRS. PORTER ONLY CALLED FOR ME BECAUSE THIS KID CAME TO HER FOR HELP.

SHE'S... UH...

MY AUNT.

MY AUNT JAY!

WHAT?

JENNY IS YOUR <u>AUNT</u>?

YES!

'JAY' FOR 'J'ENNIFER.

JENNIFER PORTER. --I'M HERE VISITING FROM THE COUNTRY.

I DIDN'T KNOW YOU HAD ANY BROTHERS OR SISTERS IN THE COUNTRY.

WELL...,

I'M NOT HER **REAL** AUNT.

SHE'S A VERY DISTANT RELATIVE.

SHE JUST GOT INTO TOWN TODAY, AND SHE'S STAYING WITH ME FOR THE NEXT LITTLE WHILE.

UNTIL MY MOTHER GETS BETTER.

SHE'S SICK WITH SOMETHING THE DOCTORS CAN'T FIGURE OUT, SO I'M STAYING HERE UNTIL SHE GETS BETTER.

AND I WAS JUST OUT WALKING TO SEE THE CITY, AND THAT'S WHEN I FOUND THAT BOY.

AND YOU WERE RIGHT. --HE ASKED ME FOR HELP, SO I WENT RUNNING.

TO MY AUNT.

SEE?! THEY'VE DONE NOTHING WRONG!

I CAN VOUCH FOR MRS. PORTER MYSELF!

HRM...

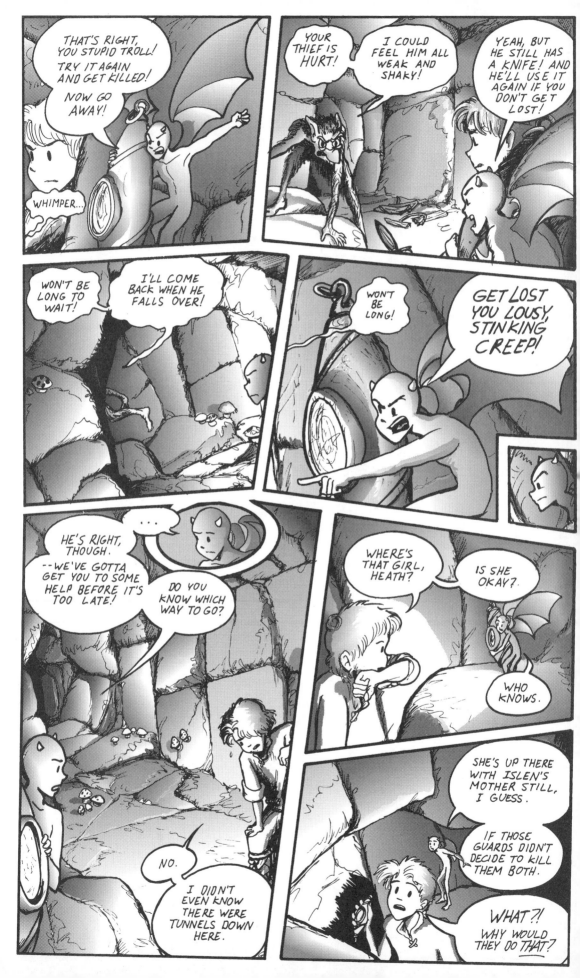

I DON'T KNOW.

THE PRINCE'S SOLDIER'S KNOW THEY'RE YOUR FRIENDS.

ERG..! YOU'RE RIGHT!

THEY COULD BE IN TROUBLE!

I HOPE THEY'RE OKAY!

WHO KNOWS.

BUT I DON'T THINK IT'S A GOOD IDEA TO GO TO MRS. PORTER'S ANYMORE.

THE SOLDIERS WILL BE LOOKING FOR YOU AT HER HOUSE.

YEAH...

I WONDER WHERE I SHOULD GO...

I FEEL REALLY BAD.

RUBEL: FOLLOW THESE. SORRY ABOUT THE WOUND Q.Z.

RUBEL: FOLLOW THESE. SORRY ABOUT THE WOUND Q.Z.

RUBEL: FOLLOW THESE. SORRY ABOUT THE WOUND Q.Z.

HEY, LOOK!

IT'S A MESSAGE!

RUBEL: FOLLOW THESE. ← SORRY ABOUT THE WOUND Q.Z.

IT'S A CHALK MESSAGE!

IT'S FROM THAT BUTT-HEAD WIZARD!

QUINTON! WOW!

HE KNEW I WAS GOING TO BE HERE!

AND HE KNEW I WAS WOUNDED!

THAT'S VERY POWERFUL MAGIC FOR HIM TO KNOW.

IT'S BECAUSE HE'S THE ONE WHO WOUNDED YOU!

WITH THAT DUMB JAQUES QUICK STORY!

I CAN'T **STAND** THAT GUY!

RELAX, VARKIAS.

COME ON.

I THINK I CAN MAKE IT IF I REST EVERY ONCE IN A WHILE.

GRUMBLE...

ERK!

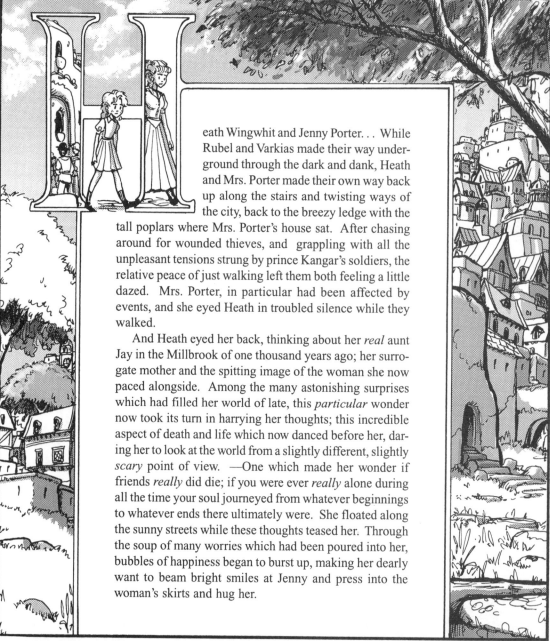

Heath Wingwhit and Jenny Porter. . . While Rubel and Varkias made their way underground through the dark and dank, Heath and Mrs. Porter made their own way back up along the stairs and twisting ways of the city, back to the breezy ledge with the tall poplars where Mrs. Porter's house sat. After chasing around for wounded thieves, and grappling with all the unpleasant tensions strung by prince Kangar's soldiers, the relative peace of just walking left them both feeling a little dazed. Mrs. Porter, in particular had been affected by events, and she eyed Heath in troubled silence while they walked.

And Heath eyed her back, thinking about her *real* aunt Jay in the Millbrook of one thousand years ago; her surrogate mother and the spitting image of the woman she now paced alongside. Among the many astonishing surprises which had filled her world of late, this *particular* wonder now took its turn in harrying her thoughts; this incredible aspect of death and life which now danced before her, daring her to look at the world from a slightly different, slightly *scary* point of view. —One which made her wonder if friends *really* did die; if you were ever *really* alone during all the time your soul journeyed from whatever beginnings to whatever ends there ultimately were. She floated along the sunny streets while these thoughts teased her. Through the soup of many worries which had been poured into her, bubbles of happiness began to burst up, making her dearly want to beam bright smiles at Jenny and press into the woman's skirts and hug her.

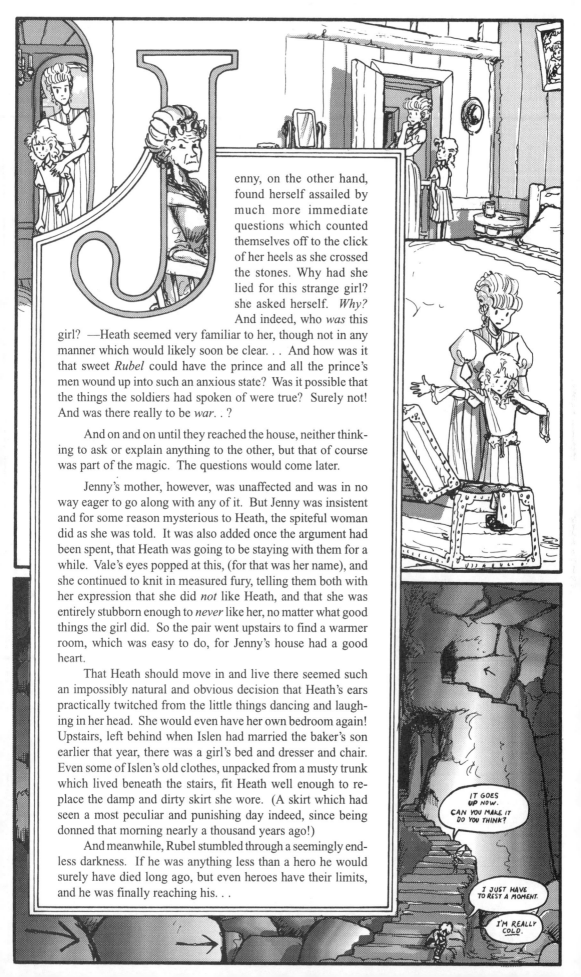

Jenny, on the other hand, found herself assailed by much more immediate questions which counted themselves off to the click of her heels as she crossed the stones. Why had she lied for this strange girl? she asked herself. *Why?* And indeed, who *was* this girl? —Heath seemed very familiar to her, though not in any manner which would likely soon be clear. . . And how was it that sweet *Rubel* could have the prince and all the prince's men wound up into such an anxious state? Was it possible that the things the soldiers had spoken of were true? Surely not! And was there really to be *war.* . ?

And on and on until they reached the house, neither thinking to ask or explain anything to the other, but that of course was part of the magic. The questions would come later.

Jenny's mother, however, was unaffected and was in no way eager to go along with any of it. But Jenny was insistent and for some reason mysterious to Heath, the spiteful woman did as she was told. It was also added once the argument had been spent, that Heath was going to be staying with them for a while. Vale's eyes popped at this, (for that was her name), and she continued to knit in measured fury, telling them both with her expression that she did *not* like Heath, and that she was entirely stubborn enough to *never* like her, no matter what good things the girl did. So the pair went upstairs to find a warmer room, which was easy to do, for Jenny's house had a good heart.

That Heath should move in and live there seemed such an impossibly natural and obvious decision that Heath's ears practically twitched from the little things dancing and laughing in her head. She would even have her own bedroom again! Upstairs, left behind when Islen had married the baker's son earlier that year, there was a girl's bed and dresser and chair. Even some of Islen's old clothes, unpacked from a musty trunk which lived beneath the stairs, fit Heath well enough to replace the damp and dirty skirt she wore. (A skirt which had seen a most peculiar and punishing day indeed, since being donned that morning nearly a thousand years ago!)

And meanwhile, Rubel stumbled through a seemingly endless darkness. If he was anything less than a hero he would surely have died long ago, but even heroes have their limits, and he was finally reaching his. . .

IT GOES UP NOW. CAN YOU MAKE IT DO YOU THINK?

I JUST HAVE TO REST A MOMENT.

I'M REALLY COLD.

YES.

RUBEL: This will heal your wound. Q.Z.

DRINK ONE OF THOSE.

I SUSPECT IT MIGHT HEAL YOU.

QUINTON BELIEVES IT WILL AT ANY RATE.

DON'T TRUST HER, RUBEL!

IT COULD BE MORE POISON!

I'VE NO NEED TO POISON HIM AGAIN.

HE KNOWS THAT.

DO YOU STILL HAVE THE PIECES OF YOU INSIDE THAT YOU HAD IN THE DREAM GARDEN?

THE PARTS THAT WEREN'T EVIL?

THE DREAM GARDEN WAS A DREAM.

YOU SAW THE FOOLISH LITTLE GIRL INSIDE ME.

I'D ALMOST BE EMBARRASSED IF IT HADN'T BEEN SO EFFECTIVE.

UNLESS A GIRL CRIES, SHE'LL NOT STEAL YOUR HEART.

PAGH!

SPEAKING OF WHICH, IT WOULD BE WISE TO KEEP YOUR NEW FRIEND AWAY FROM ME.

IF HEATH AND I MEET, THERE'S NO TELLING WHAT WOULD HAPPEN.

I WILL KEEP HER PRESENCE HERE A SECRET FROM MY MASTERS AND MY PEERS.

THIS MUCH I CAN DO FOR YOU.

BEYOND THAT, HOWEVER, I'M AFRAID I MIGHT BECOME QUITE HOMICIDAL.

Chapter 5

MRS. PORTER..!

WHY, SMITH ROBINS!

HELLO! I'M GLAD I CAUGHT YOU!

I JUST CAME BY BECAUSE I WANTED TO APOLOGIZE FOR ALL OF YESTERDAY'S TROUBLE. --WITH YOUR NIECE AND THAT THIEF.

WE NEVER DID FIND HIM...

OH! WELL..!

UM, I SUPPOSE THINGS COULD HAVE GONE MUCH WORSE.

BUT THANK YOU FOR STANDING UP FOR US.

I'D DO IT ANY TIME!

I DON'T KNOW WHAT THOSE MEN THINK BEING A SOLDIER IS ALL ABOUT...

BULLYING CIVILIANS AND ALL...

IT'S ALL THIS BUSINESS OF GOING TO WAR, I GUESS, BUT I STILL DON'T LIKE IT!

ANYWAY, I HOPE YOUR NIECE IS OKAY. --IT'S TOO BAD, GETTING THAT SORT OF GREETING ON HER FIRST DAY INTO TOWN.

OH, SHE'S FINE.

JUST A LITTLE QUIET RIGHT NOW.

SHE'S STILL VERY WORN OUT FROM HER JOURNEY.

WELL, IF YOU EVER NEED ANYTHING...

BUT I MUST GET GOING! --I CAN'T EVEN STOP FOR A MOMENT!

I JUST WANTED TO SEE HOW YOU WERE. --YOU'VE NO IDEA THE SORTS OF ERRANDS THE PRINCE HAS US RUNNING AROUND ON!

WELL, YOU MUST PROMISE TO STOP BY WHEN YOU'VE MORE TIME TO SPEND!

IT WAS A DIFFICULT ONE, I THINK.

I WILL! --BYE JENNY!

GOODBYE, SMITH ROBINS!

GO TO SLEEP NOW, DEAR.

IT'S LATE.

TOMORROW IS GOING TO BE A VERY BUSY DAY. AND WITH ANY LUCK, RUBEL WILL SHOW UP.

I HOPE SO!

I'VE BEEN WORRYING ABOUT HIM SO MUCH!

AND I HARDLY EVEN KNOW HIM...

I KNOW IT'S BECAUSE WE'RE BOTH CONNECTED TO EVERYTHING, AND ALL THAT... BUT IT STILL SEEMS WEIRD.

I KNOW I KNOW...

BUT YOU MUSTN'T WORRY...

IT'S TRUE.

MOST PEOPLE DON'T REMEMBER, AND FOR ME IT'S MORE A DREAM THAN A MEMORY.

BUT SINCE YOU TOLD ME WHAT YOU HAVE, I BELIEVE IT!

EVERYONE REMEMBERS THE WOLF THOSE YEARS BACK WHEN IT CAME SKULKING DOWN THE STREET...

HEAVEN KNOWS *HOW* IT GOT OVER THE EAST WALL..!

EVERYONE REMEMBERS, BUT NOBODY SEEMS TO *BELIEVE*.

IT'S THE SAME WITH RUBEL.

HE'S A MAGIC BOY.

JUST LIKE YOU'RE A MAGIC GIRL.

—BUT YOU'RE *MY* MAGIC GIRL, NOW...

AND YOU'RE MORE REAL THAN *HE* IS.

I GUESS... EXCEPT I CAN'T SEEM TO GET *MY* MAGIC TO WORK.

HM... PERHAPS THAT'S JUST AS WELL...

PERHAPS YOU'LL *STAY* REAL.

AS LONG AS YOU'RE REAL, YOU'LL HAVE SOMEWHERE TO CALL *HOME*.

YEAH, I KNOW. WEIRD, HUH?

I CHECKED IT OUT ONCE, BUT THERE WAS NOTHING THERE.

MY GRANDFATHER SAID IT WAS JUST THE STONE REFLECTING HEAT, OR SOMETHING.

ANYWAY, THE SPECIAL THING ABOUT THAT TOWER IS THAT IF YOU GO TO IT,

—AND IT'S REALLY HARD TO FIND WHEN YOU'RE ACTUALLY IN THE WOODS...
—I KNOW THE WAY, THOUGH.

BUT WHEN YOU GO TO IT, THERE'S THIS SECRET PATH LEADING AWAY FROM IT.

AND THE PATH IS IMPOSSIBLE TO FIND IF YOU DON'T GO TO THE TOWER FIRST.

I'VE TRIED.

ANYWAY, THE PATH LEADS YOU TO A GULLY WHERE THERE'S A BIG STONE BOX WITH A MONSTER IN IT.

THE MONSTER'S NAME IS CHEAD.

CHEAD?!

WE'RE NOT GOING TO HIM, ARE WE?

THAT'S A BAD IDEA, RUBEL!

EVEN YOU SAID IT'S STUPID TO ASK HIM QUESTIONS!

WHAT IF YOU CAN'T ANSWER HIS RIDDLE?

WHAT THEN?

AND ANYWAY, THE WISHING KEY IS STILL MISSING!

I KNOW.

THAT'S WHY I HAVE TO GO LOOK FOR IT.

I'LL COME BACK WHEN I FIND IT AND GET EVERYTHING READY TO GO.

OR WE'LL GO TOMORROW IF IT'S TOO LATE.

I'M GOING TOO?

everal years back, when Rubel was a younger boy with different friends, he had gone on an adventure called the *Roam,* and as with many of Rubel's adventures, it had taken its inspiration from a tale Quinton had once told. . .

Quinton used to live, a long time ago, in a small village on the skirts of a bronze and dusty empire deep in the south. One day when recalling his time there, Quinton explained to Rubel how the boys in those days, before they turned into men, would be driven by main force from the village to live in the wilderness for a period of days and weeks. —It was a test, pitting boys against the wild with nothing but their wits to preserve them. They weren't even allowed to take their shoes with them! The search for manhood had to be done barefoot. It was very symbolic.

As the Roam grew to be an older and older tradition, it eventually became a thing made almost *entirely* of symbols rather than real things. Once, much earlier on, when there had been no symbols at all, the boys had been sent off entirely *naked;* without even a scrap of clothing on! —Though as with many ancient rites, safety conscious adults alarmed by the barbarity of such details modified things. It was decided that the boys ought to be allowed clothes; that they should instead be sent *barefoot.* Going barefoot, it was agreed, should be enough to stay in touch with nature. —Or fulfill whatever purpose going naked was originally meant to satisfy. (That is, unless it was meant to be anything more than a way of making the test of manhood all the more unpleasant.) In any case, there was no need to be uncivilized about it.

hus, by dribs and drabs the Roam was watered down. Obscure little elaborations, —special hats and speeches and whatnot, were introduced, all designed to appear impressive enough to make up for all the watered down parts. In later centuries, village boys no longer set forth, frightened and brave, to march across the wilderness. The Roam had devolved into little more than a backyard picnic affair where family and friends would gather to watch their sons of age speak memorized words and pace about in silly patterns upon a patch of dirt shoveled in especially for the occasion.

Though to Quinton's scheme of thinking. . , (as with all things when observed through the bright lens of his imagination), the significance of the Roam sprang up and roared once again, vital and strong, filled to brimming with its old essence. And when he told *Rubel*, (who's imagination was no less brilliant), the young thief's eyes shone and he understood at once, immediately determining that he *too* must embark upon a Roam and he made preparations to do so. (Though he wouldn't go naked. His grandfather decided this very firmly. —And as well, he would also carry a knife wherever this Roam might take him, which would NOT be to the forest. As always, his grandfather was most emphatic about this last item.)

After wrestling with the problem, Rubel also decided that he ought to take his friends with him; Islen and Dyme Dun, and his dog and Varkias. (This was as it ought to be, he reasoned, since they would be initiating the whole *group,* not just him.) Furthermore, they really *wouldn't* go naked, because there was a girl with them and because she would have nothing to do with it, (and because Dyme Dun was too ashamed). When Rubel lost this argument for the second time, he conceded that going barefoot *did* sound like it would probably be enough to stay in touch with nature, though he did make a profound point of forgetting to carry his pocket knife. But at any rate, they roamed off barefoot *together* that morning, as the Monster Slayers. That was the important thing.

Their adventure didn't last for days and weeks. It lasted just one afternoon, though this proved more than enough time for them to get in deep over their heads. Other than Rubel, who had been strictly forbidden to visit the forest, (but regularly did anyway), Islen and Dyme Dun were not the sort of kids who even *needed* forbidding. The forest was simply not a place people went, and everybody knew it. —Not unless people were looking to vanish forever. The Sleeping Wood was a place to fear.

But Islen and Dyme Dun were Rubel's sorceress and knight, and they had seen enough in his company to know that the Monster Slayers were something necessary. And besides, even if he did suggest peculiar things sometimes, (like tromping through the woods with no clothes on), Rubel was the sort who loved his friends very much, and who his friends in turn trusted and marveled at. Baily, the dog went because he would have followed Rubel anywhere; he and Rubel played and chased about in the streets, and Baily was respected by other dogs for his position at the young thief's side. Only Varkias knew better than to go into the woods, having been bound by promises and oaths and magic and such, making it his job to complain and grumble the whole way, which he did faithfully. —Though not so insistently that anybody might take notice and consider turning back, for he loved going on adventures with Rubel more than anything else in the world. And so they went, all five.

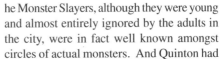

he Monster Slayers, although they were young and almost entirely ignored by the adults in the city, were in fact well known amongst circles of actual monsters. And Quinton had prepared them. He had given Islen a Sorceress's staff which was shaped and painted in such a way that monsters feared its sight and burned at its touch. Dyme Dun was given a wooden short sword which could cut through muscle and bone as well as any metal; it too was magic and monsters were scared of it. Rubel didn't need any special weapons or magic because he was already a thief, and Varkias and Baily didn't need special things either, because Varkias was an imp, and a dog was a dog.

The Monster Slayers were a real band, and over the course of three years they fought and killed countless vile monsters, many imaginary, but some real, including one which had lived beneath Dyme Dun's bed, (and alternatively behind the dresser when Dyme's mother dusted). Rubel's Monster Slayers were smart and strong and they knew no fear. But they had not yet met Chead.

Chead was the sort of monster who wasn't scared of Quinton's magic trinkets, or of dogs or imps. Or even thieves. Chead was a very old monster, who had lived and terrorized the land for many ages. He had eventually been defeated, long ago, by an army of brave knights and powerful wizards who had locked him away in a magical stone prison and then forgot about him. Chead was also the kind of monster that didn't die, and he was still just as strong and dangerous as he had always been; perhaps even more so, after having been locked up with his own bitterness for so very long.

The forest, roused by the Monster Slayer's march, and annoyed by their arrogance, decided to teach them fear that day. With grumbles and sighs, the Sleeping Wood led them down pathways and ravines to the foot of the great tree where Chead's stone box sat wedged between the two immovable roots which had held it in a jailer's embrace for so many countless ages.

The door of the box was bolted shut with a massive lock made entirely from silver, but which had been weathered black by all the years. And hanging from a peg upon the face of the door was a long golden key, blazing in the sunlight, as big as Rubel's arm from elbow to wrist. It was before this awesome sight the Monster Slayers arrived and stood in wonder.

arkias, whose memory was normally small and unreliable, now caused him to catch his breath. A wisp of something from long ago moved like a tendril of old smoke in his mind, but it was only a residue and Varkias' brain was not a complicated enough mechanism to recognize its significance. He only knew to feel cautious and wary and distrustful, but when he made noises to this effect he was ignored. —He had been making such noises ever since reaching the forest and they had all long stopped paying attention. The box was breathing.

Great sighs, like a horse's huffs, but deeper and much heavier blew in and out so that the Monster Slayers could feel the warm, breathy gusts from the cracks of the box. Whatever huge bellow lungs lived inside the box, they sucked air in and out like some leathery machine. And then they spoke.

"Is somebody out there?" it came, not loud, but deep and powerful enough to make them all feel something rumble inside themselves. "Who is out there? I hear little hands and little feet pickering about my prison. —Could it be? Is it that they have sent *children* after all this time to rattle my lock and laugh at me through the cracks; to snatch away the last shreds of my dignity?" the voice asked, heavy with an old and tired resentment.

"No," Islen replied, "We didn't come to laugh. We didn't even know you were in there."

There was a pause and a sound of shuffled movement from within as something very large shifted its weight. It spoke again, but this time with a hazy quality to its words, which was both difficult to concentrate on and dizzying to ignore.

"If you are not the children of my captors. . , then. . ." There was a long, thoughtful pause. "On the side of my prison which is warmed by the sun, there is a small crack; just were the wall meets the ceiling stone. Many seasons of seeping water turning to ice, and many days of crumbling sunlight have widened that old crack so it is large enough now for me to see the forest and the sky. . . Might I ask that you put your faces to the crack so that I may look upon you as well?"

The Roamers were hesitant, but in the end decided that no harm could come from only looking, and did so, one after the other. Rubel went first, but could see almost nothing for the dark, but Chead could see *him*. . .

h, a fine and honest face!" he declared. "You are the leader of this mysterious band? Will you not tell me who you are?"

"We are the Monster Slayers. We are five great friends," Rubel replied. "A knight and a sorceress and a thief! And a fine dog and a magical imp. And we have powerful weapons made by a powerful wizard at our disposal!"

"My!" Chead exclaimed, sounding very impressed. "The Monster Slayers! With magic and imps and weapons and dogs! You must be very famous! —But I did not know that they entrusted such a serious task as monster slaying to people so young. Well! Times have certainly changed since I was put here! You must be very important people in the city!"

With these words, Rubel was very flattered and as a result let slip much of the caution and common sense he should have kept under such circumstances, but this was of course Chead's intent. Chead had learned long ago how to get the things he wanted by telling people what they liked to hear.

"Well, actually nobody really knows that we protect the city from monsters. We kind of do it without anybody telling us. Nobody believes in monsters anymore." Rubel admitted with an effort, though he felt compelled to stretch the truth, or even to lie outright. The spell which misted Chead's words was meant not only to encourage a loose tongue, but also to draw its listeners into binding themselves with their own boasting. Though while Rubel was unsophisticated and easily trusting in his early years, he had learned to prize honesty over the respect of strangers, so was able to resist. "We are on a Roam," he offered proudly, as if to make up for the fact that he wasn't famous.

Chead frowned in the darkness as the spell slipped from Rubel. The boy stepped down and helped up his friend, and while Chead exchanged some few words with Dyme Dun, he thought very hard. (A clever monster can both think about one thing and talk about another.) And when it was Islen's turn to peek through the crack, he had come up with a new plan. "Ah!" he sighed. "A Roam. I went on a roam once. Long before they put me in here. . ." He fell silent.

"Why were you put in here?" Islen peeped after a time. It seemed quite abruptly to her that it was awful for anybody to be locked up like this. Chead was slow to reply.

"I am ashamed. .," he said softly, "to speak of that. . . But then I suppose that is a fitting thing. . ." He was quiet for a space and then admitted in a shame filled voice, "I once did a very bad thing, long ago. . ."

The children waited without a noise for him to go on. He did so in sad, apologetic tones. . .

WELL, I CAN
TRY TO SOAK OUT
THE BLOODSTAIN...
BUT IN THE MEANTIME,
I'LL LOOK IN LAWRENCE'S
OLD THINGS FOR
SOMETHING YOU
CAN WEAR.

When I was not locked here; when I was free to live as others do, the king and all the people in the city allowed their children to laugh at me and call me names." He hesitated. "I am. ., quite *large* and quite ugly, you see. But I could not do anything about it, for I was not allowed to get angry.

"They told me I was strong, so I should not be hurt by such little things as names. Except it *did* hurt, and nobody would *believe* when I said so. They just scoffed at me. —But then one day it hurt so badly that I *did* grow angry. . . I know I should not have, but I couldn't help it, and I knocked down the boy who was leading the laughter. I *am* very strong, and the boy hit his head on the ground and died.

"Everybody was very angry with me, and it didn't matter how much I apologized or how badly I felt. A boy had been killed and that was that. The king called for a stone prison to be made deep in the forest, and he sent his knights to arrest me. They brought me out here and locked me up in this box, and they told me that they would only let me out once I had learned my lesson."

The children were all stricken.

"But you didn't mean to! You didn't mean to kill the boy, did you?"

"No. But I knocked him down on purpose, and there is no excusing that."

"But he was making fun of you!"

They were all deeply moved by the story.

"And the knights never came back to let you out?" Rubel asked.

Chead did not answer right away. "Well, I think that perhaps maybe I *haven't* learned my lesson. And they are still waiting until I have. . ?" He said this, quietly pleading Rubel to agree with him.

"I am very, very sorry for what I did. But they never come to check. And it's been so long. ., but what other reason can there be?"

The children all thought they knew, but said nothing. After an almost palpable moment of tortured consideration, the beast took another long and shaky breath, one so choked with sorrow that only pity was twisted from the children's hearts. "Except *sometimes*. ., I think that maybe they have might have forgotten all *about* me. Or even that. . . I sometimes *think,* that maybe. ., *maybe* they never *meant* to come back. That maybe they never wanted me at *all*. That nobody *ever* wanted me. . ."

They all had tears in their eyes now. All but Varkias.

"No, no! He's lying," the imp insisted. "He is! He is! Listen to me!"

But, "Quiet, Varkias," they said. And they unlocked Chead's prison.

Chapter 6

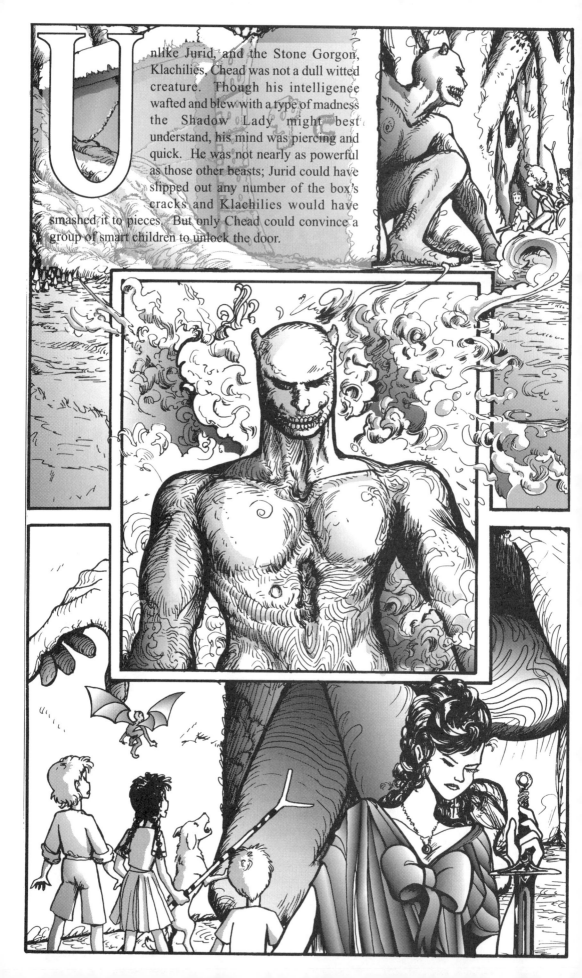

nlike Jurid, and the Stone Gorgon, Klachilies, Chead was not a dull witted creature. Though his intelligence wafted and blew with a type of madness the Shadow Lady might best understand, his mind was piercing and quick. He was not nearly as powerful as those other beasts; Jurid could have slipped out any number of the box's cracks and Klachilies would have smashed it to pieces. But only Chead could convince a group of smart children to unlock the door.

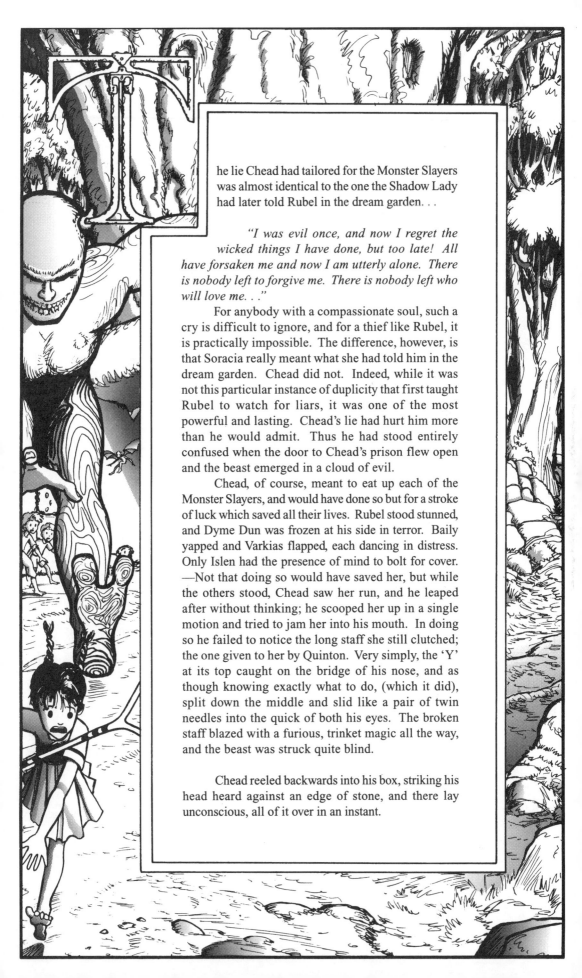

he lie Chead had tailored for the Monster Slayers was almost identical to the one the Shadow Lady had later told Rubel in the dream garden. . .

"I was evil once, and now I regret the wicked things I have done, but too late! All have forsaken me and now I am utterly alone. There is nobody left to forgive me. There is nobody left who will love me. . ."

For anybody with a compassionate soul, such a cry is difficult to ignore, and for a thief like Rubel, it is practically impossible. The difference, however, is that Soracia really meant what she had told him in the dream garden. Chead did not. Indeed, while it was not this particular instance of duplicity that first taught Rubel to watch for liars, it was one of the most powerful and lasting. Chead's lie had hurt him more than he would admit. Thus he had stood entirely confused when the door to Chead's prison flew open and the beast emerged in a cloud of evil.

Chead, of course, meant to eat up each of the Monster Slayers, and would have done so but for a stroke of luck which saved all their lives. Rubel stood stunned, and Dyme Dun was frozen at his side in terror. Baily yapped and Varkias flapped, each dancing in distress. Only Islen had the presence of mind to bolt for cover. —Not that doing so would have saved her, but while the others stood, Chead saw her run, and he leaped after without thinking; he scooped her up in a single motion and tried to jam her into his mouth. In doing so he failed to notice the long staff she still clutched; the one given to her by Quinton. Very simply, the 'Y' at its top caught on the bridge of his nose, and as though knowing exactly what to do, (which it did), split down the middle and slid like a pair of twin needles into the quick of both his eyes. The broken staff blazed with a furious, trinket magic all the way, and the beast was struck quite blind.

Chead reeled backwards into his box, striking his head heard against an edge of stone, and there lay unconscious, all of it over in an instant.

None of them held any illusions that they had done anything brave or clever in defeating the beast. After pushing the great door shut again and locking it securely, they turned their Roam around and went back home, each quite shaken. They took the golden key with them, meaning to hide it somewhere in order to prevent anybody from making the same mistake they had done, and when Mrs. Porter took it away and gave it to a city guardsman, they didn't complain. They figured it would be lost enough like that. And it was.

But that was not the end of it. . .

A monster that can't see isn't much good to anyone, least of all, himself. The power inside Chead was very old and it filled him and drove him like an engine. —And now that it was trapped in a blackness which, because of his ruined eyes, was made far deeper than the inside of any stone box could be, it roiled and steamed, utterly *boiling* in hatred. Thus, prying and frustrated, the magic searched within Chead's hurting body, and because it was powerful, and because it was ancient, it eventually found a way. . .

HEY HEATH.

WHAT'S UP?

VARKIAS?! IS THAT YOU?

YEAH. I'M INVISIBLE NOW.

INVISIBLE? YOU LOOK LIKE A SEA-SHELL!

HEY! WATCH IT!

I'M JUST CARRYING THIS THING!

WHAT HAPPENED?

HOW DID YOU TURN INVISIBLE?

IT'S MERMAID MAGIC!

MERMAIDS?

YEAH.

RUBEL THOUGHT IT WAS GETTING TOO DANGEROUS TO HAVE EVERYBODY SEEING ME IN THE CITY, AND SARA SAID SHE COULD HELP.

SARA?

YOU MEAN THAT GHOST-GIRL CHAINED UP UNDER THE CITY?

THE ONE AND ONLY.

HE WENT BACK TO SEE HER LAST NIGHT. —THEY TALKED ALL NIGHT LONG!

HE GAVE HER BACK THE LANTERN.

REALLY..? GEE...

I GUESS SHE WAS HAPPY TO SEE HIM.

I GUESS.

SHE SAID IF SHE WASN'T A GHOST, SHE WOULD HAVE KISSED HIM.

ANYWAY, SHE HAS SOME FRIENDS NOW.

SOME MERMAIDS.

OH.

WOW. REAL MERMAIDS?

YEAH. GIRLS WITH FISH TAILS.

GEE.

WERE THEY PRETTY?

I DON'T KNOW. I GUESS. THEY TURNED ME INVISIBLE.

HOW?

WITH MAGIC OIL FROM UNDER THE SEA.

IT COMES IN TWO SHELLS. HERE.

SMEAR SOME OF THAT ON YOUR EYE-BALLS.

WHAT?

YOU HAVE TO.

THE OIL FROM THE OTHER SHELL I SMEARED ALL OVER MY SKIN AND IT TURNED ME INVISIBLE.

THE MERMAIDS WERE USING IT TO HIDE BECAUSE THERE'S SOME EVIL SEA-WITCH WHO WANTS TO KILL THEM FOR BEING FRIENDS WITH SARA.

YOU CAN'T SEE THEM AT ALL UNLESS YOU PUT SOME OF THAT STUFF IN YOUR EYES.

WILL IT STING?

A LITTLE.

BUT YOU HARDLY NOTICE IT AFTER.

ANYWAY, WE ALL HAVE TO REMEMBER TO USE NEW OIL EVERY TIME THE MOON GOES FROM BEING A FULL MOON, TO BEING NOTHING, TO BEING FULL AGAIN.

THAT'S WHEN IT WEARS OFF.

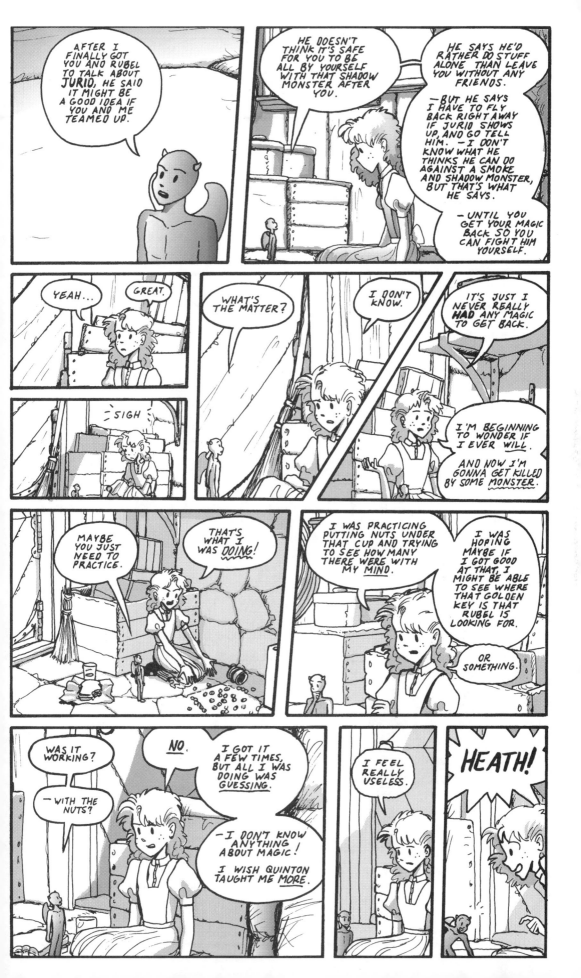

COMING, MRS. ZELGA!

LUNCH TIME IS OVER!

THERE'S A PILE OF DUST LEFT BEHIND THE COUNTER!

THAT'S NOT WHERE IT BELONGS.

OKAY. I'LL COME AND SWEEP IT.

MRS. ZELGA?

SHE'S MY AUNT'S FRIEND. SHE OWNS THE PLACE.

I WORK HERE ON TUESDAYS, WEDNESDAYS AND THURSDAYS.

OH.

WHAT DAY IS IT TODAY?

TUESDAY.

Rubel spent many more days than he had anticipated following the trail of the key. (He had been anticipating only one.) —The key was, however, much more magical than anybody suspected or gave it credit, and it had made up its mind to be difficult. It had also a long time in which to get lost. After all, Rubel was only a little boy when Jenny Porter gave it to the guardsman those years ago.

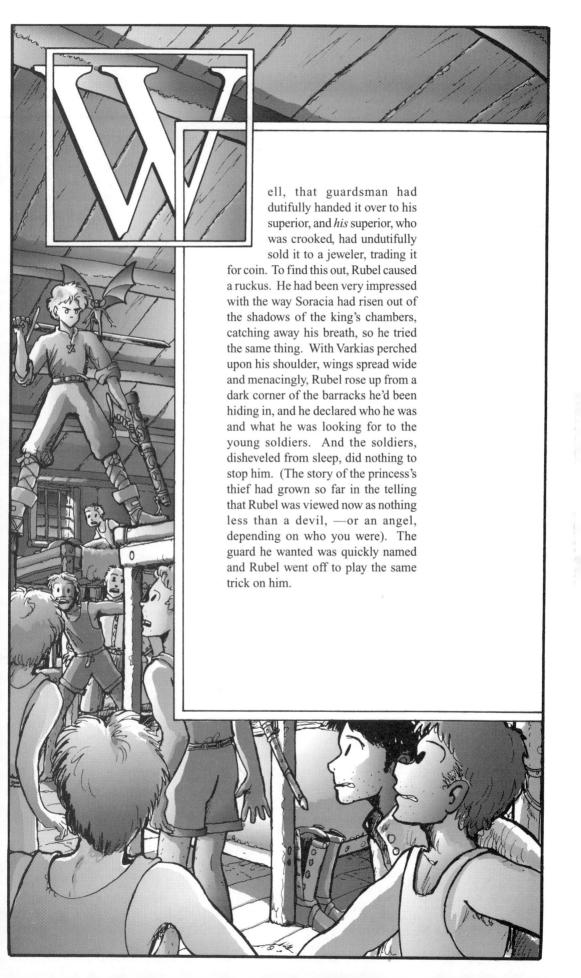

Well, that guardsman had dutifully handed it over to his superior, and *his* superior, who was crooked, had undutifully sold it to a jeweler, trading it for coin. To find this out, Rubel caused a ruckus. He had been very impressed with the way Soracia had risen out of the shadows of the king's chambers, catching away his breath, so he tried the same thing. With Varkias perched upon his shoulder, wings spread wide and menacingly, Rubel rose up from a dark corner of the barracks he'd been hiding in, and he declared who he was and what he was looking for to the young soldiers. And the soldiers, disheveled from sleep, did nothing to stop him. (The story of the princess's thief had grown so far in the telling that Rubel was viewed now as nothing less than a devil, —or an angel, depending on who you were). The guard he wanted was quickly named and Rubel went off to play the same trick on him.

This man, to whom Jenny had handed the key, had been recently (and unfairly) retired from the king's guard with whom he'd served all his adult life. He did not like the prince or the prince guard and he told Rubel so, and offered to help. Varkias was rather put out when the man did not cower in fear as the others had done, but Rubel was very pleased and made up a speech on the spot, telling him that things would get much worse before they got better, but that the day would come when everyone of true spirit would be called upon to rise up against evil and villainy. The man was moved to tears by the noble words and he swore himself again to his king and to the princess, Katara. Rubel left with the information he wanted and a very good feeling in his heart, insisting that this encounter was better by far than frightening a bunch of young soldiers in their barracks. Varkias grumbled.

In this manner, Rubel followed the trail of the key. The jeweler who had bought it was beguiled by the craftsmanship and by the magic from which they key had been made, and he could not bring himself to melt it down. Instead, he kept it in his private collection, wrapped in a piece of blue velvet cloth. His wife, however, (with whom he was ever at odds), *did* want to melt it down, and she told her brother about it, with whom she planned to steal it. The jeweler woke the night of the theft, and was struck by his wife's brother, who fled. During his flight, however, the foul-brother was himself robbed, by a small-time thug who Rubel managed to hunt down and question concerning that night three years ago. The key, he learned, had traveled to the docks, and into the possession of the dreaded, Black Casper.

he dread pirate, Black Casper, once the scourge of the ocean ways, feared even by the king's navy, lost his ship years ago to a sea monster, and decided instead to come ashore and burrow himself into the darker corners of Oceansend. Black Casper was both very clever and very brutal; a scoundrel to the bone, and he drew about himself him a brood of pirates and criminals so feared that the underworld dared only whisper. He and his men worked in shadows, terrorizing all, and to whom every docks-man, honest or not, had to pay his due or wake up dead. Upon crossing Black Casper's path, Rubel decided right away that when he had finished with all his other obligations, he would drive the pirates from his city. Indeed, he killed nearly half a dozen that very night when confronting Casper about the key. The old pirate got away and swore a vengeance so bitter that his own men shivered in their boots, but he had also told Rubel where the key had gone next and the thief vanished at once to follow. (Varkias enjoyed their encounter with the pirates best of all, and he sang a silly tune with rhyming words of how Rubel had chased the pirates around and around their pirate's den.)

That's when things got bogged down.

Heath knew all about this part, because Rubel came to her for help.

What happened to the key after the pirates was this: There was a simple-minded boy named John, who worked in Black Casper's den and who slept in a corner upon a pile of moldy straw. His job was to run to and fro on little errands and be kicked about by the pirates when they were feeling ugly and mean, which as a rule, was always.

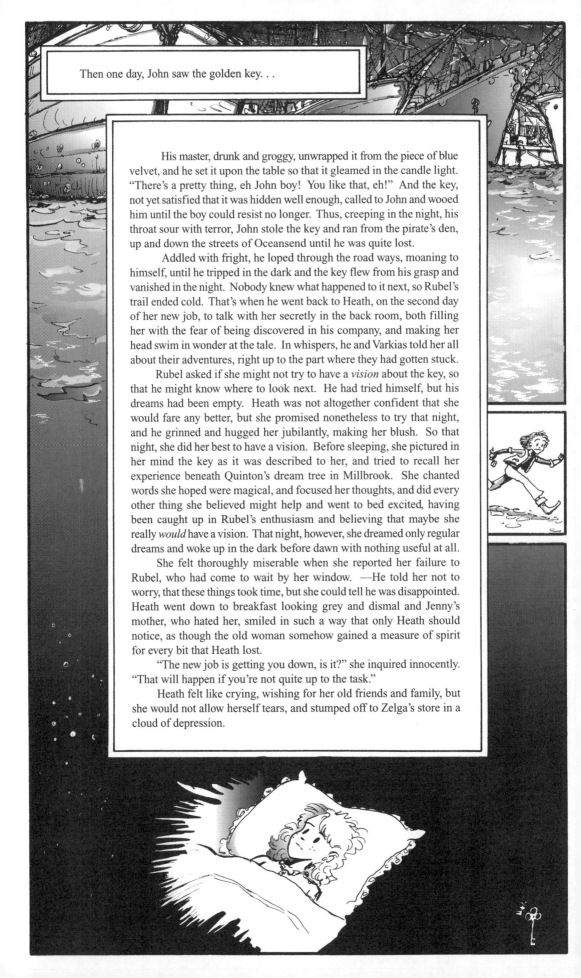

Then one day, John saw the golden key. . .

His master, drunk and groggy, unwrapped it from the piece of blue velvet, and he set it upon the table so that it gleamed in the candle light. "There's a pretty thing, eh John boy! You like that, eh!" And the key, not yet satisfied that it was hidden well enough, called to John and wooed him until the boy could resist no longer. Thus, creeping in the night, his throat sour with terror, John stole the key and ran from the pirate's den, up and down the streets of Oceansend until he was quite lost.

Addled with fright, he loped through the road ways, moaning to himself, until he tripped in the dark and the key flew from his grasp and vanished in the night. Nobody knew what happened to it next, so Rubel's trail ended cold. That's when he went back to Heath, on the second day of her new job, to talk with her secretly in the back room, both filling her with the fear of being discovered in his company, and making her head swim in wonder at the tale. In whispers, he and Varkias told her all about their adventures, right up to the part where they had gotten stuck.

Rubel asked if she might not try to have a *vision* about the key, so that he might know where to look next. He had tried himself, but his dreams had been empty. Heath was not altogether confident that she would fare any better, but she promised nonetheless to try that night, and he grinned and hugged her jubilantly, making her blush. So that night, she did her best to have a vision. Before sleeping, she pictured in her mind the key as it was described to her, and tried to recall her experience beneath Quinton's dream tree in Millbrook. She chanted words she hoped were magical, and focused her thoughts, and did every other thing she believed might help and went to bed excited, having been caught up in Rubel's enthusiasm and believing that maybe she really *would* have a vision. That night, however, she dreamed only regular dreams and woke up in the dark before dawn with nothing useful at all.

She felt thoroughly miserable when she reported her failure to Rubel, who had come to wait by her window. —He told her not to worry, that these things took time, but she could tell he was disappointed. Heath went down to breakfast looking grey and dismal and Jenny's mother, who hated her, smiled in such a way that only Heath should notice, as though the old woman somehow gained a measure of spirit for every bit that Heath lost.

"The new job is getting you down, is it?" she inquired innocently. "That will happen if you're not quite up to the task."

Heath felt like crying, wishing for her old friends and family, but she would not allow herself tears, and stumped off to Zelga's store in a cloud of depression.

BOY, I CAN'T WAIT UNTILL FRIDAY!

WHAT HAPPENS ON FRIDAY?

THAT'S ONE OF MY MAGIC DAYS.

JENNY SAYS I CAN PRACTICE MAGIC AND DO WHATEVER I WANT ON FRIDAY AND SATURDAY.

THOSE ARE **MY** DAYS IN THE WEEK.

HOW MANY DAYS ARE THERE IN THE WEEK ALTOGETHER?

SEVEN.

AND YOU ONLY GET TO HAVE *TWO* OF THEM?

WELL, I HAVE TO WORK HERE. —TO EARN MY KEEP.

BUT I THOUGHT MRS. PORTER WAS TAKING CARE OF YOU.

ME AND RUBEL GET TO HAVE ALL OUR DAYS IN THE WEEK.

WELL LA-DEE-DA FOR YOU!

AT LEAST I DON'T GET SHOT AT ALL THE TIME!

RUBEL LIKES GETTING SHOT AT.

HUMPH!

GOODBYE FLORENCE.

BYE, ZELGA.

OKAY, HEATH. YOU'RE WAITING FOR ME, AREN'T YOU.

COME IN THEN, WILL YOU PLEASE?

COMING.

THERE NOW. THIS IS YOUR PAY FOR LAST WEEK.

WOW!

I WASN'T EXPECTING SO MUCH.

OPEN

HM. THIS IS THE FIRST TIME YOU'VE RECEIVED PAY FOR WORK?

IT ADDS UP, DOESN'T IT?

NOW MAKE SURE YOU DON'T LOSE ANY OF IT!

OPEN

I WON'T!

VARKIAS, WHERE IS QUINTON'S TOWER?

WHY?

YOU WANT TO GO THERE?

YEAH!

I'VE BEEN THINKING THAT THERE'S PROBABLY SOME BOOKS UP THERE WITH SOME **REAL** SPELLS I COULD TRY.

I WANT TO FIND THEM!

HEY...

I NEVER THOUGHT OF THAT.

THAT'S A GOOD IDEA!

AND THEN YOU COULD LEARN TO FLY, LIKE THE SHADOW LADY!

AND MAYBE EVEN SHOOT FIRE!

WOW!

I BET YOU COULD BEAT JURID EASY, THEN!

THAT'S RIGHT!

I CAN'T AFFORD TO SIT AROUND WAITING FOR QUINTON TO GET BACK.

—AND FOR RUBEL TO DO EVERYTHING ON HIS OWN.

AW, FORGET QUINTON.

HE MESSED EVERYTHING UP!

YOU'RE PROBABLY THE ONLY ONE WHO CAN FIX ANY OF IT!

Chapter 7

WHEW!

WHAT A CLIMB!

WHY WOULD ANYBODY BUILD HALF THEIR CITY ON A MOUNTAIN?

COME ON. QUINTON'S TOWER IS JUST OVER THERE.

KANG! PANK! KANG!

KANK!

ACK! SOLDIERS!

THERE'S BLUE-BACKS HERE!

WE'VE GOTTA HIDE!

HUM! LOOK AT THEM.

WHAT DO YOU THINK THEY'RE DOING?

OKAY.

HOLD ON. —THERE MUST BE SOME...

WHAT ARE YOU LOOKING FOR?

IF THIS IS QUINTON'S TOWER, HE'LL HAVE MADE SURE THERE WOULD BE SOME USEFUL THINGS GROWING NEARBY...

CRASH!

HRM!

WHAT IS IT?

NEEDS A CATALYST.

MUNCH.

HMM...

AH! RIGHT!

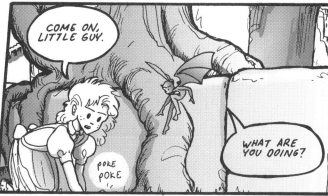

COME ON, LITTLE GUY.

POKE POKE

WHAT ARE YOU DOING?

GO ON. I'M POKING YOU. I WON'T MIND.

THOSE ARE ANTS.

ZOW!

WHAT ARE YOU DOING?

YOU WANTED IT TO STING YOU?

WOW!
I SCARED
THEM AWAY!

THAT
WORKED
GREAT!

THEY'LL
COME BACK
SOON, THOUGH.

I'M WORRIED
ABOUT THOSE
IRON GUARDS
YOU AND RUBEL
TOLD ME ABOUT.

THEY DON'T
HAVE SKIN TO
PRICK. AND I BET
THE SMELL OF LEAVES
WON'T AFFECT THEM EITHER!

OOH...
THAT'S
RIGHT.

COME ON.
WE HAVE
TO HURRY.

IS THIS
WHERE
QUINTON
KEEPS HIS
MAGIC
BOOKS?

I DON'T
KNOW.

OH, BUT
I DO REMEMBER...

DON'T TOUCH
ANYTHING
THAT SAYS:
"DO NOT TOUCH."

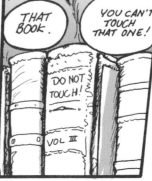

THAT
BOOK.

YOU CAN'T
TOUCH
THAT ONE!

DO NOT
TOUCH!

VOL III

WHY
NOT?

I KEEP TELLING EVERYBODY, QUINTON'S USELESS.

HE'S **GOT** TO HAVE SOMETHING. WE JUST HAVE TO FIND IT!

THERE'S LOTS OF BOOKS HERE!

...WERE STUNG AS THEY WERE WORKING ON THE DOOR. -- THEIR WHOLE FACES SWELLED RIGHT UP!

TRICKS AND JAPES! NOTHING LETHAL.

AND YOU ARE TELLING ME YOU DID NOT GET INSIDE?

THE DOOR IS MADE OF STONE, M'LADY!

PAINTED TO LOOK LIKE WOOD!

NO.

THERE IS NO DOOR.

THERE ARE STAIRS.

THIS TOWER IS ENCIRCLED WITH ILLUSIONS.

THAT TREE.

BURN IT DOWN, AT ONCE!

THERE WILL BE NO MORE STINGS AND ILLUSIONS!

YOU.

THIS WHOLE AREA MUST BE CORDONED OFF! I WANT AT LEAST A HUNDRED MORE TROOPS UP HERE!

WHY THERE WERE SO FEW DISPATCHED..!

THOSE FOOLS!

YOU!

RIDE TO THE PALACE AND INFORM THE PRINCE, DIRECTLY!

HAVE HIM SEND ANOTHER OF MY SISTERS.

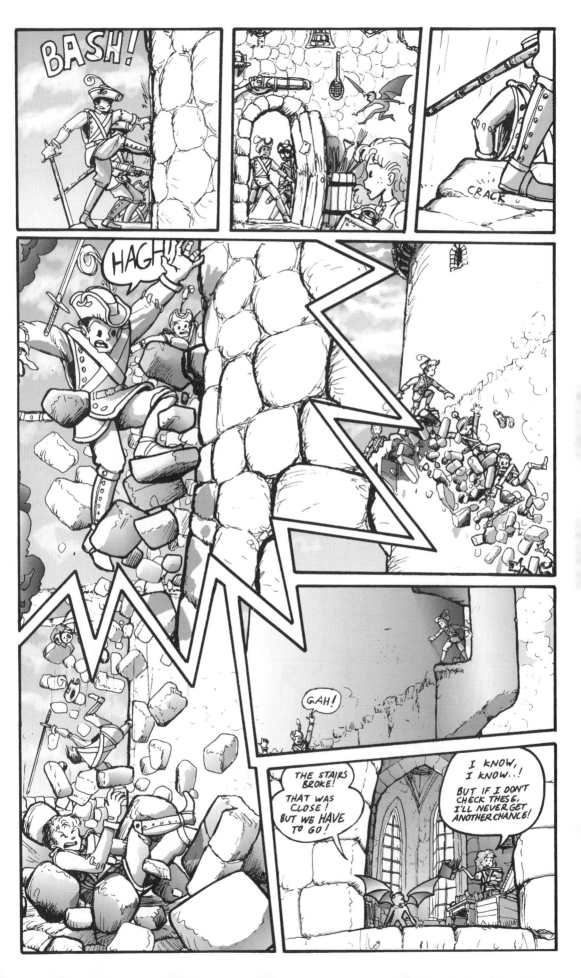

WAH...

Quinton had gone to some trouble to design his tower. It was made in such a way that upon self-destruction, the falling debris would only land upon a section of the city below where nobody lived anymore. The reason for this was that for the last twenty years, Quinton had randomly pushed large stones over the edge of his spot on the mountain side. He called these rocks 'falling hazards' and told people to beware of the day when a great whopping piece of the mountain might slide off and crush everybody below. Quinton never got caught at these missions of vandalism, and his falling hazards regularly punched holes in rooftops and caused general anxiety and eventually people *did* move away from that spot at the foot of the mountain. Varkias, who was in an unusually reflective mood, chattered about all of this to both Rubel and Heath as they made their way back home, dusty and tattered in the warm setting sunlight. Heath listened and grinned and laughed and felt wonderfully light as she walked alongside her brave and brooding thief.

After a while, Rubel's brooding began to make her feel uncomfortable so she began chattering too, in an effort to break his silence.

"I can't believe we lived through that!" she declared a little too brightly. "What an adventure! I hope Quinton doesn't mind that we ruined his tower."

She smiled at him fondly, but Rubel only huffed angrily and barked back at her, "Heath!"

She stopped short, confused.

"I'm really mad, Heath!" he said hotly. "That was really dangerous! If you wanted to look for books, you should have asked me to go up there for you. And not just because of all the fighting. —If that witch survived, or if any of those guards who saw you survived, they'll be able to connect it back. They'll know who you are and that you're in the city! Soracia is the only one on their side who knows right now who you are, and that's bad enough, but at least she promised to keep it a secret. *She* knows what's at stake. If the rest of them find out you're here, you'll be in real trouble! And it won't be just you. It'll be Mrs. Porter, and her mother and Islen and maybe even Islen's husband. And it'll be the lady who hired you in her store, and *everybody* you've made friends with since you got here. The prince's guards will come and arrest them *all* and take them away and he'll question them, and when they can't answer his questions, he'll have them tortured, and when they still can't answer him, he'll have them *killed*. Do you *get* it, Heath? The prince is *really* dangerous, and Locumire is working with him. You have to be a *lot* more careful. You can't just think about what *you* want. You can't just think about yourself!"

Heath was caught entirely off guard. She hadn't considered any of these things. She stood before Rubel, holding the big spell book tightly against her stomach as though it might absorb the impact of his words. Rubel looked at her without sympathy.

"I'm sorry," she breathed, her voice gone. "I just wanted to find something to learn magic from. . . I just wanted to help."

Rubel said nothing and looked past her, sighing in flat resignation. "Come on. What's done is done, I suppose. You better get inside. Mrs. Porter's really worried."

They were outside the house, and Heath suddenly wanted to go anywhere but inside to face Jenny. What would she say? Then a thought struck her and she felt quite sick.

"What is it?" Rubel asked, seeing all color drain from the girl's face. She turned her eyes up at him. They swam.

"I lost the money from my job," she said weakly. "And the parcel Mrs. Zelga asked me to take to Jenny. I put them down somewhere. It all fell down with Quinton's tower. . ."

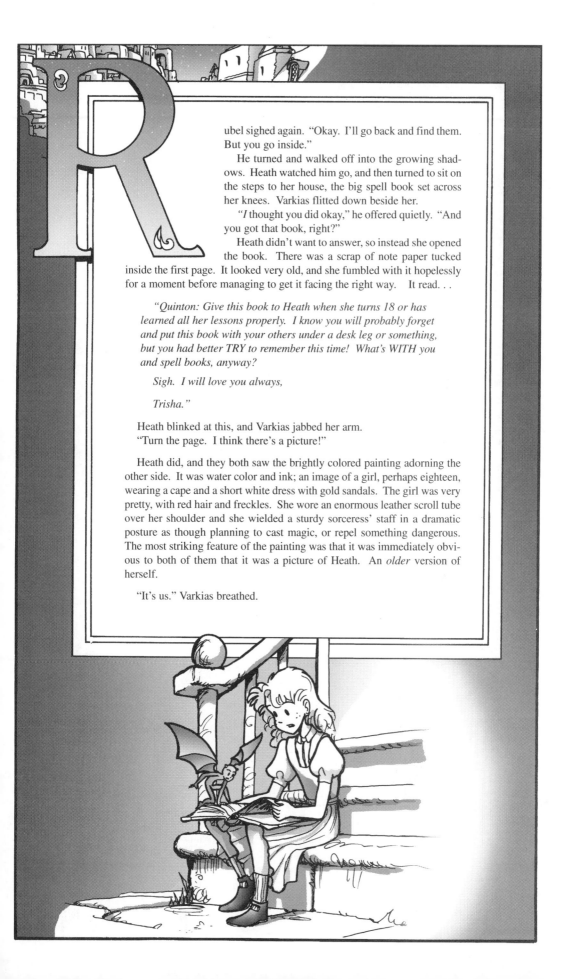

ubel sighed again. "Okay. I'll go back and find them. But you go inside."

He turned and walked off into the growing shadows. Heath watched him go, and then turned to sit on the steps to her house, the big spell book set across her knees. Varkias flitted down beside her.

"*I* thought you did okay," he offered quietly. "And you got that book, right?"

Heath didn't want to answer, so instead she opened the book. There was a scrap of note paper tucked inside the first page. It looked very old, and she fumbled with it hopelessly for a moment before managing to get it facing the right way. It read. . .

"Quinton: Give this book to Heath when she turns 18 or has learned all her lessons properly. I know you will probably forget and put this book with your others under a desk leg or something, but you had better TRY to remember this time! What's WITH you and spell books, anyway?

Sigh. I will love you always,

Trisha."

Heath blinked at this, and Varkias jabbed her arm.
"Turn the page. I think there's a picture!"

Heath did, and they both saw the brightly colored painting adorning the other side. It was water color and ink; an image of a girl, perhaps eighteen, wearing a cape and a short white dress with gold sandals. The girl was very pretty, with red hair and freckles. She wore an enormous leather scroll tube over her shoulder and she wielded a sturdy sorceress' staff in a dramatic posture as though planning to cast magic, or repel something dangerous. The most striking feature of the painting was that it was immediately obvious to both of them that it was a picture of Heath. An *older* version of herself.

"It's us." Varkias breathed.

He was right. At the Sorceress's shoulder was a little drawing of Varkias, penned with ink and filled in with grey paint. Varkias and Heath exchanged a look.

"What does it say?" Varkias asked excitedly, indicating the flowing hand written inscription beneath the picture.

Heath read it aloud, her heart racing:

"Hello, Heath. Here's a painting of me when I wrote this book. I hope Varkias is still with you. I put him in the picture too. It's a picture of us fighting monsters or something. Quinton believes you will probably look exactly like me. That's only supposed to happen once every thousand years or so. Was he right? I hope you find this book to be of some help. In case she's still bugging you, I put some extra spells in it designed especially to deal with Locumire. Use them carefully, and good luck!

"Quinton also asked me to add this: Never stop believing in yourself, no matter what people say. But I think you have to take that advice with moderation. If you're anything like me, then you sometimes get carried away with things and hurt those around you. It's the balancing act of life, and I'm afraid we are sometimes not very good at it. But here's something to keep in mind when things do go sour: I've learned that in the end, so long as you keep the best intentions at heart, people will always hold more love for those who act than for those who do not. That's just the way it is."

Yours, (Ours,) Trisha Ringlet.

HEATH..?

Chapter 8

oracia held
out the plain wooden
stick before her. Rubel
moved toward it, lured. But
he also knew that her eyes were
upon him, and he drew in his
breath sharply against the things he
felt when so close to her. She smelled
like autumn leaves, and her nearness
caused his flesh to tingle and his heart to
race. She had not had such an effect on him
in the Dragon's garden. There, she had just
been a troubled friend, but now she was a Shadow
Queen at the height of her powers! With his jaw
set hard, Rubel chanced a look at her face and slipped
almost at once into her eyes; they held him and he swam;
they were cold and gleaming and perfect. She smiled,
moving back with the stick and Rubel followed. With a
turn she stepped from the ledge and slipped through the air.
Rubel lunged to chase after her.

"Hey! I *need* that!" He called. "Stop playing these games!"

She laughed again and danced away and he scrambled to follow.

Soracia felt wonderful. Normally, she was a serious,
frightening creature, but tonight she was filled with a thrill of
happiness which bounced within her like a big laugh seeking
release. She swirled through the night like a joyful wraith,
leading Rubel on a tireless chase over the rooftops of Oceansend.
To the sleepless and the sleepy who caught glimpses of them,
they were a pair of supernatural dancers who flitted between the
stars and window wells.

"It is the princess and her thief!" they thought, mistaking Soracia
for her sister, and either feared or marveled, depending on who
they were.

And though he tried, Rubel could not catch her. —Perhaps on
another night he might have; his powers *were* growing steadily,
but tonight Soracia was feeling at home for the first time in many
ages, and her heart felt truly free. Each past failure had only been
a stepping stone to *this* night, and she casually let them slide from
her concern. Every twirl and laugh was brilliant and heartfelt and
right. Her head was light as though drunk, but her thinking was
as clear and crisp as winter air. Even in these foreboding days,
her dark oaths and her master's hand, and all the things that hurt
her and bound her, all of it melted away in the moonlight.
Tonight, nothing could touch her! Not even a thief; not unless
she chose.

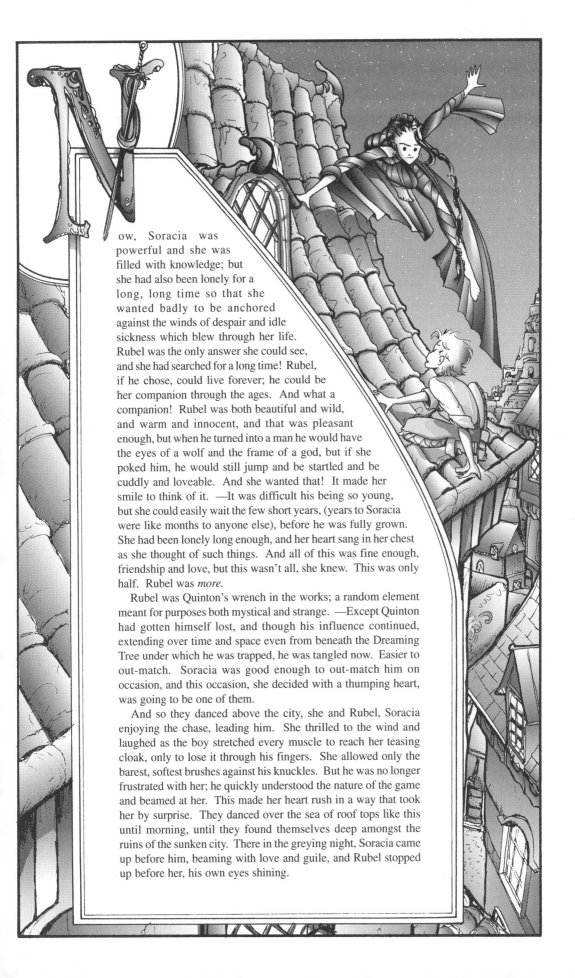

ow, Soracia was
powerful and she was
filled with knowledge; but
she had also been lonely for a
long, long time so that she
wanted badly to be anchored
against the winds of despair and idle
sickness which blew through her life.
Rubel was the only answer she could see,
and she had searched for a long time! Rubel,
if he chose, could live forever; he could be
her companion through the ages. And what a
companion! Rubel was both beautiful and wild,
and warm and innocent, and that was pleasant
enough, but when he turned into a man he would have
the eyes of a wolf and the frame of a god, but if she
poked him, he would still jump and be startled and be
cuddly and loveable. And she wanted that! It made her
smile to think of it. —It was difficult his being so young,
but she could easily wait the few short years, (years to Soracia
were like months to anyone else), before he was fully grown.
She had been lonely long enough, and her heart sang in her chest
as she thought of such things. And all of this was fine enough,
friendship and love, but this wasn't all, she knew. This was only
half. Rubel was *more.*

Rubel was Quinton's wrench in the works; a random element
meant for purposes both mystical and strange. —Except Quinton
had gotten himself lost, and though his influence continued,
extending over time and space even from beneath the Dreaming
Tree under which he was trapped, he was tangled now. Easier to
out-match. Soracia was good enough to out-match him on
occasion, and this occasion, she decided with a thumping heart,
was going to be one of them.

And so they danced above the city, she and Rubel, Soracia
enjoying the chase, leading him. She thrilled to the wind and
laughed as the boy stretched every muscle to reach her teasing
cloak, only to lose it through his fingers. She allowed only the
barest, softest brushes against his knuckles. But he was no longer
frustrated with her; he quickly understood the nature of the game
and beamed at her. This made her heart rush in a way that took
her by surprise. They danced over the sea of roof tops like this
until morning, until they found themselves deep amongst the
ruins of the sunken city. There in the greying night, Soracia came
up before him, beaming with love and guile, and Rubel stopped
up before her, his own eyes shining.

ubel, though he knew little about love, was strong and clear in what he *did* feel. And it was not just youthful lust, for there was that. —He had been her friend when he was small, and her enemy recently, going so far as to almost hate her and certainly to fear her. But now, something else was happening. With his own magic drawing him ever further from the world of normal people, leaving even little Varkias confused, he was lonely and more than a little worried about where it all might leave him. He was still without close friends; indeed, since her arrival, Varkias had seemed pre-occupied with Heath, asking questions and talking about her, to the point where Rubel began to wonder if the imp might not actually be in love with the girl. A most peculiar thing for an imp! —And then Rubel had discovered the spell book which Quinton used to prop up the wobbly bed leg in his tower. Rubel found it days before anyone else, and when he opened it and saw the painting of older Heath with Varkias at her shoulder, it was clear to him the pair had a history together which went much further back than his ever did. This revelation caught at his heart in a strange way, making him feel wistful and left out.

He said to himself that he would give the book to Heath the very next day, but when the next day came, he was feeling sad and so didn't. And when he hunted for the key with Varkias in the night, their bond seemed strained somehow, like a promise finally fulfilled and no longer of vast importance. He killed pirates and brigands in frustration, and worse, he'd known that the Shadow Lady was watching quietly from a dark corner; watching him and expressing dark sympathy and love. This scared him, and he did not give the book to Heath on the next day either, as though holding it back kept him from slipping into Soracia's world. He held on to it the next day after that also, keeping it under the bed leg. Indeed, when he had gotten angry with Heath after she went to Quinton's tower to find the book for herself, it was for more reasons than he said or really understood, and afterwards he felt more alone than ever. While young Heath was bright and charming, and while he was her sworn thief, she was still new. She was distant from the worlds he moved through now, so he didn't think to talk to her about his troubles. Or to Varkias. Heath had taken away his best friend! In fact, it seemed to him that she had already found more friends in the city than *he* had. —He knew this was his own fault, that if he had chosen to live with Mrs. Porter when she offered, things would have been differ-ent. He knew that he was not the sort of person who could fit into the world like that, but understanding this didn't make it hurt any less.

nd so in the night, with all these feelings pent up and aching within him, an old emotion reared its head; much stronger this time than before. —A wave of compassion for the Shadow Lady filled him; compassion and *hope* that maybe she really *was* the one person he could be with and truly be not alone. That Soracia was finally the one who could best love him and understand.

He had been right in what he said to the king; that he was a thief and would not be easily tricked by a beautiful sorceress. —And if it had just been a matter of lust, he certainly could have made himself like a metal box to her, his body and soul steeled and untouchable. But this was something *else*. And of course, all these things Soracia knew; she knew about the book and about how friends and love worked at every level of intricacy, and she played it all to her advantage.

She was aware also, however, of a nagging sense deep in her mind which asked if perhaps she hadn't fallen rather more deeply in love with Rubel than she ought to have done. Love can always trick away reason, no matter how much a person might have or how long one might have had it. She wondered, but dismissed it. —Love for her was rare and she wanted it, and all the pieces were falling properly this time, so she threw away her caution and went forward. But when sunlight dawned like a beacon through the grey sky and caught their faces in a guilty light, a voice came forth from beyond the grave. A voice, hurt and disappointed.

"Oh, Rubel. . ," it came. The voice of a ghost girl, the one of Rubel's friends who would have understood, but who he had forgotten once again. Rubel's breath caught within him and he spun around to see Sara's pale face, and Soracia felt her moments of freedom evaporate with the sunlight, to be lost in the morning mists above the sunken city.

I WAS VISITING WITH SARA BLUE, AND SHE SAID THAT ONE DAY, RUBEL WILL JUST BE A **SHAFT OF SUNLIGHT** AND A **BREATH OF WIND,** AND NOBODY WILL BE ABLE TO SEE HIM UNLESS HE ALLOWS IT.

AND THE SHADOW LADY BETTER WATCH OUT, BECAUSE HE'LL BE STRONGER THAN ANYBODY THEN!

AND SARA ALSO TOLD ME NOT TO WORRY SO MUCH.

SHE SAID THAT THE SHADOW LADY ONLY HAS RUBEL **HALF BOUND** TO HER.

SHE SAID IT'S IN HER NATURE; THE SHADOW LADY IS THE **QUEEN OF HALVES,** AND SHE CAN NEVER GET AWAY FROM THAT NO MATTER HOW HARD SHE TRIES.

EXCEPT I'M STILL WORRIED.

RUBEL KISSED HER LAST NIGHT.

WHAT?

HE KISSED HER?

HE **KISSED** THE SHADOW LADY?

MY SISTER?

YEAH.

WELL HOW EXACTLY DID **THAT** HAPPEN?!

I DON'T KNOW. I ONLY SAW IT FROM FAR.

SHE BLEW ME AWAY ON A PUFF OF AIR.

I HATE WHEN SHE DOES THAT.

SHE KNOWS IF I'M AROUND, RUBEL WILL LISTEN TO ME!

SEE, WHAT HAPPENED WAS WE FOUND OUT THAT THE MOUSE-KINGS GAVE THE KEY TO A **GARGOYLE** TO PROTECT, SO WE WENT TO THE GARGOYLE TO WAIT AROUND TILL DUSK, AND ASK HIM ABOUT IT, BUT WHEN WE GOT THERE, HE WAS DEAD!

AND HIS HANDS WERE CUT OFF!

RIGHT THROUGH THE STONE!

RUBEL THOUGHT FOR SURE IT WAS THE SHADOW LADY, SO THEN WE WENT LOOKING FOR HER.

THAT'S WHEN SHE BLEW ME AWAY, SO ALL I COULD DO WAS WATCH FROM THE DISTANCE.

SHE SHOWED HIM A PLAIN OLD STICK, BUT SHE TRICKED HIM AND HE THOUGHT IT WAS THE KEY!

IF I WAS THERE, I COULD HAVE TOLD HIM IT WAS JUST A MAGICAL ILLUSION.

—LIKE THE STAIRS.

BUT RUBEL IS BAD WITH MAGIC, SO HE GOT FOOLED AND STARTED CHASING HER.

CHASING HER?

ALL OVER THE CITY!

—I COULD HARDLY KEEP UP!

AND AFTER A WHILE I THINK THEY WERE STARTING TO HAVE FUN.

AS IF SHE **WANTED** HIM TO BE AFTER HER, AND HE **LIKED** CHASING.

LIKE PLAYING A GAME. BUT IT WAS STILL HOT AND ANGRY SORT OF.

THEN BY THE END OF THE NIGHT, THEY ENDED UP DOWN IN THE SUNKEN CITY.

AND THAT'S WHERE SHE KISSED HIM.

UGH!

WAS IT ON THE **LIPS?**

I DON'T KNOW. I WAS PRETTY FAR... —I **GUESS** SO.

DID THEY HAVE THEIR ARMS AROUND EACH OTHER?

YES.

OH...

AND HE WASN'T TRYING TO STOP HER OR ANYTHING?

I DON'T KNOW EXACTLY.

ANYWAY, THAT'S WHEN SARA SHOWED UP AND INTERRUPTED THEM.

THE SHADOW LADY GOT REALLY ANGRY!

SHE BLASTED SARA, AND SARA SAID IT HURT EVEN THOUGH SHE'S A GHOST.

AND THEN THE SHADOW LADY THREW HER SWORDS AT RUBEL AND THEY SPUN AROUND HIM AND WOULDN'T LET HIM GET AWAY.

BUT THEN SHE **DID** LET HIM GO AND SEEMED FRIENDLY AGAIN, AND SHE KISSED HIM ONCE MORE, BUT JUST A SMALL KISS, AND THEN SHE FLEW AWAY.

AND SO I FLEW UP TO RUBEL TO FIND OUT WHAT HAPPENED, AND HE GOT ANGRY WITH ME AND DIDN'T WANT TO TALK ABOUT IT AND HE STOMPED AWAY.

SO I HUNG OUT WITH SARA FOR A LITTLE WHILE, AND THEN I WENT TO YOUR PLACE.

OH.

I GUESS THAT'S NOT SO GOOD, HUH?

GOOD MORNING, HEATH!

MR. MERRICE STOPPED BY WITH AN ORDER FOR SOME CRYSTAL. —THE TWO CRATES IN THE BACK NEED TO BE UNPACKED, AND EACH GLASS CHECKED FOR CHIPS AND REWRAPPED IN CREPE CLOTH AND THEN PUT BACK.

OKAY.

SO, DID YOU FINISH MEMORIZING ANYTHING WHEN I CAME IN THIS MORNING?

‹PFF.‹ WHO CARES..?

I DO.

‹SIGH‹

I DON'T KNOW.

I FINISHED ONE, SORT OF...

THE "FIND IT" SPELL?

"THINGS LOST MAY BE FOUND AGAIN," IS WHAT IT SAID.

IT SEEMED LIKE AN EASY SPELL TO START WITH.

PLUS, MAYBE IT CAN HELP FIND THE KEY.

THAT'D BE GOOD, I SUPPOSE.

DID YOU MEMORIZE ENOUGH TO TRY IT OUT?

I DON'T KNOW.

IT WASN'T SO MUCH WORDS AS IT WAS PICTURES.

MEMORIZING PICTURES ISN'T THE SAME AS READING.

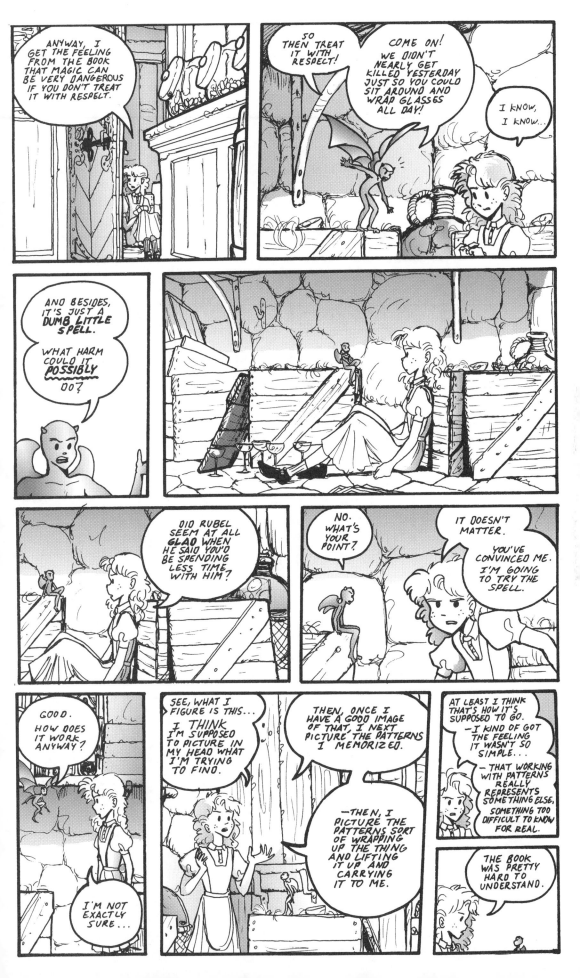

HM. ARE YOU GOING TO TRY TO FIND THE KEY?

YEAH. —DESCRIBE IT TO ME AGAIN.

THREE RINGS AT ONE END, LIKE A CLOVER, LONG STEM, TWO TEETH, AND ALL GOLD.

OKAY THEN... HERE GOES.

BLINK

IS THAT IT?

YEAH.

NOTHING HAPPENED.

DO WE HAVE TO WAIT? HOW LONG IS IT SUPPOSED TO TAKE?

I DON'T KNOW.

I DON'T THINK IT WORKED.

OH, BLEH. I HAVE **NO** IDEA WHAT I'M DOING. THIS IS POINTLESS!

NO, NO! TRY SOMETHING ELSE!

I JUST GOT THIS PIECE IN THREE WEEKS AGO.

RUMAGE

AH! HERE WE GO!

AHH! HA! HA!

WHAT'S GOTTEN INTO YOU?

OH, NOTHING. I'M JUST HAPPY, IS ALL.

WELL, THAT'S GOOD. —YOU LOOKED LIKE A LITTLE RAIN CLOUD WHEN YOU CAME IN THIS MORNING!

HAVE YOU FINISHED WITH THOSE GLASSES? I NEED THEM BY NOON.

NO. NOT YET.

WELL, YOU HAD BETTER GET THEM DONE.

OKAY. I'LL GO DO THEM.

IT'S A FINE FABRIC. —MADE BY ONE OF THE GYPSY WOMEN WHO SELLS TO ME.

WHAT A FUNNY GIRL!

IT'S PERFECT! EXCELLENT! I'LL TAKE THE LOT OF IT!

WOW!

YEAH, BUT IT WASN'T THE REAL ONE, EITHER, WAS IT?

Last Page of the Story.

This third book represents an exciting point for me.

Back in the days when this story and its characters were a jumble of pictures on piles of typing paper, —and electronic notes to myself spread across dozens of magnetic disks from one of those old computer systems which would crash if you filled up all of its memory. (Writing more than forty nine pages at one time would do this); back in *those* days, I had some very clear ideas as to what *Thieves & Kings* was meant to be.

It wasn't *really* going to be just the story about a young thief who lived in a magical city. And while this book may seem like it, it's not the story of a young girl from across time trying to find a home and learn the secrets of magic. It's not Heath's story either. Of course, Rubel and Heath are both wonderful, vital characters of whom I am very fond, but they are only two pieces. The real story is not about just them, but the whole mesh of people surrounding them, and how they all fit together. It's about the *city*. Cities are interwoven, living machines; clockworks of people and things, all working to be *alive*. These first three books have put all the pieces on the board; everything I think I will need to make it go. And they complete the first 'arc' (to use a much over used term) of a three part story.

The princess Katara hasn't been around in ages; we've missed most of her childhood, (which is partly why I've been focusing so much on Heath's). Katara is sixteen years old now, and she has been raising an army in the forest. I'm a little scared of what will happen when I start publishing her story. It's sometimes dangerous to build up a character too much, because it can be a let-down when they finally show up. (I'm only a *little* worried, though. I've already started work on her story, and it promises to be really neat!). Still, with Katara comes war, and eventually all stability will fly out the window. I've not written or drawn a war yet. Mountains are going to split. —And I've only finished *building* those mountains! I don't want to take them down just yet.

Anyway, Heath and Rubel have finally reached a point where they can stop running. They can gather their wits and spend some time growing up, and I intend to give them the space to do that. For a while.

And that's the reason I'm so pleased about having reached this point in the story. I've been day dreaming for years now! I can think of a dozen stories from the top of my head that I've been wanting to tell, and dozens more which come to mind constantly. I'll have to pick and choose carefully; Oceansend is a city with ten thousand of years worth of secrets buried beneath her stones. And at long last it's time to go looking for them. . !

I am a very fortunate writer!

Take care!
—Mark Oakley

The End